Nude Mice

And Other Medical Writing Terms You Need to Know

Cynthia L. Kryder
2009
www.theaccidentalmedicalwriter.com

Nude Mice

And Other Medical Writing Terms You Need to Know

By

Cynthia L. Kryder, MS, CCC-Sp

With a foreword by Brian Bass

About the Author

Cyndy Kryder has worked in the field of health care in some way ever since she grabbed her Master's Degree and headed to her first professional job as a speech-language pathologist at a private school in suburban Philadelphia. Her later 9-year stint working in a pediatric-rehabilitation hospital developed her passion for writing patient-education materials and cemented her interest in the field of medicine. She launched her freelance medical writing career in 1992 and is thankful for the freedom and flexibility it offers her.

Cyndy currently writes promotional, educational, and scientific pieces for professionals and lay audiences in a number of different therapeutic areas and for a wide range of media. She also assists companies in their publication-planning efforts. A member of the Delaware Valley Chapter of the American Medical Writers Association (AMWA), Cyndy presents workshops and leads roundtable discussions on various topics for freelance medical writers and editors.

In 2008, Cyndy and her colleague, Brian Bass, formed a company and made a commitment to develop books for individuals interested in pursuing freelance medical writing as a career. Their first book, *The Accidental Medical Writer*, describes their indirect and different paths to successful freelance medical writing careers. Subsequent books in the series focus on different aspects of freelance medical writing and provide tools for aspiring freelance medical writers.

You can reach Cyndy at http://www.theaccidentalmedicalwriter.com. You can also follow her on Twitter: http://twitter.com/cyndyandbrian.

Dedication

To my family. Thanks for sharing my successes as well as my failures, and for agreeing to order out from Rocco's occasionally when a deadline approaches. I love you guys!

Foreword

When I started in medical writing, I had already been a professional writer for 6 years. And while I was still in school, my favorite assignment was to write papers. So I felt pretty confident in front of a keyboard. But by the time I finished my first day as a medical writer, I felt like I was a blithering idiot.

I had just started work for an advertising agency whose clients were all in animal-health pharmaceuticals. The day began with a start-up brainstorming meeting for an ad campaign we were assigned to develop for our client's new product, an equine anthelmintic. Equine *what*!? Now, I knew that equine meant horse. But what the heck was that other word? I could barely say it, let alone figure out how to spell it. The rest of the day didn't go much better. I was bombarded with so many new words that, at first, I thought maybe I had made the wrong career move. After all, how could I be successful if I couldn't even figure out what people were saying? Then I thought better of myself.

Armed with my medical dictionary and a few other medical reference books, I thought to myself, "I can do this. If a medical student can learn it, so can I." From then on, I treated every day like I was in school. I soaked up everything I could, made notes to myself, and then challenged myself to put what I had learned to use by speaking with my colleagues and writing. That helped me to think through the processes and internalize them. Slowly, the new language I was learning began to make sense. But it wasn't easy. It took a lot of time, and I made a lot of mistakes along the way. Some of those mistakes still make me blush to think that I could have been so naïve!

If you're starting out like I did, a professional writer with no prior experience in the health care field, you'll probably feel like I felt at first, too. Dazed and confused, overwhelmed and underprepared. But perhaps you're starting like Cyndy did, a health care professional with no prior experience as a writer. I hate to tell you, but you're still in for an uphill ride. Cyndy knew a lot about this stuff before she started writing, and she was overwhelmed by the language of health care, too! Face it, no matter from which direction you come to medical writing, learning the language will be a challenge…at first. The good news is, this book is going to make it a lot easier!

When Cyndy first came up with the idea for *Nude Mice* (that title still makes me chuckle), I thought it was fantastic! We talked about how we both struggled to learn the language of health care, the language of medical writers, when we got started. It wasn't easy. Sure we had medical dictionaries, and they were invaluable. And as the Internet took off, it became easier to research terms, and particularly acronyms, online. We also each had our arsenal of books on grammar and style to help keep us on the straight and narrow. But we realized that none of these tools helped us overcome the linguistic confusion we encountered, and that we still encounter, on a daily basis. Words that sound the same but are spelled differently and have completely different meanings. Words with the same prefixes or suffixes that seem like they should pertain to the same thing, but do they?

Cyndy agreed to write this book to finally unravel the complex language that is medicine, so you can overcome the linguistic challenges you will face throughout your career as a medical writer. It's the book we both wish we'd had long ago so we could separate the Greek from the Latin, the HMOs from the CROs, the viscous from the viscus; and so we'd know a nude mouse when we saw one. It's like the old Chinese proverb, "Give a man a fish and he will eat for a day. Teach a man to fish and he will eat for the rest of his life." Here, Cyndy does a fantastic job of teaching you how to fish out the meaning of the words every medical writer needs to know to become successful. Bon appétit!

---Brian Bass

Table of Contents

Ignorance Isn't Always Bliss

Imagine this scenario. You've been hired by a medical communications firm to create a slide deck for a live symposium that will be presented during the annual meeting of a national medical specialty organization. The therapeutic area is infectious disease, an area in which you haven't worked before. Your client expects you to participate in a start-up teleconference to learn more about the project, discuss the project's parameters, and develop a timeline for deliverables (standard procedure for almost all projects). Because you haven't received any background information yet, you're at somewhat of a disadvantage.

The conference call begins, and you listen carefully as your client talks about a disease that sounds something like "mer–suh." Sometimes she calls it "C–A mer–suh," other times it's "H–A mer–suh." Then she talks about something called "ick–ack" and the IDSA. She discusses the need to focus a portion of the slides on empirical treatment of SSTIs and to incorporate new prevalence information from a recent MMWR article at some point in the presentation.

Huh?

This previous scene isn't fictional. It actually happened to me when I took on my first project in infectious disease. I had been working as a freelance medical writer for several years, yet I was a newbie in this therapeutic area and didn't know the lingo. You might not want to hear this, but in the field of medical writing each therapeutic area has its own unique jargon (that means verbal or written shorthand) and terminology. And that's jargon with a capital J.

Let me give you one example. The acronym CA means *cancer* to an oncologist (that's a cancer specialist), but to an infectious-disease doctor it stands for *community acquired*.

Here's another example. The acronym ED means *erectile dysfunction* (think Viagra®) to the urologist, but to the physician working in the emergency room, it means *emergency department*.

Those are just two examples, but you get the idea. The meanings change depending on the therapeutic area in which you are writing. And if you're talking about erectile dysfunction when your client's talking about something entirely different, it can be quite embarrassing.

So although I was familiar with the terms and abbreviations for the fields in which I had been working—cardiology, rehabilitation, and women's health—I was rather ignorant when it came to communicable diseases. Not having any background information before the conference call made it even more of a challenge.

You've probably already been in the situation where you talk to your doctors or other health care professionals and they sound as though they are speaking in a foreign language. It's common, and folks in the medical profession are notorious for using jargon that a layperson can't interpret.

Even though I had a quasi-medical background, when I first began working in a hospital I was confused. (You can read more about my background in our book, *The Accidental Medical Writer.*) Sitting in the cafeteria, I listened to conversations that were peppered with acronyms and abbreviations. The nurses and doctors were using jargon as though their lives depended on it. Instead of saying high blood pressure, they said hypertension; for high cholesterol, they substituted hypercholesterolemia. The person in charge of seeing that patients' services were covered by third-party insurers talked about

HMOs, PPOs, CPT codes, and ICD-9.

The field of biomedical communications is no different. That's why having a great medical dictionary is important. Even more so, though, is the need to have a clear understanding of some of the unique medical writing terms and acronyms you'll encounter. Because as I learned in that first infectious-disease discussion, feeling ignorant does not promote confidence in your skills, no matter what industry you're working in.

That's the purpose of this book. When my business partner, Brian, and I were discussing topics for books in our series, we knew from past experience that it would be important for aspiring medical writers to have a reference source that accomplished two purposes. First, it introduced them to certain terms that are unique to medical writing and the health care and pharmaceutical industries in general; and secondly, it defined acronyms and abbreviations in numerous therapeutic areas. Now that I think about it, there's a third purpose, too. We want this book to give you tools to enable you to figure out unfamiliar terms when you encounter them. We've filtered through the multitude of resources out there so that we can point you to the ones we consider to be useful.

This book is not a reference on English grammar and usage. There are already many excellent sources on that subject (see the resources section at the end of this book for some titles). Nor is this book meant to be a medical dictionary. Browse the shelves of your local bookstore and you can see just how many medical dictionaries already exist.

This book is meant to serve as a tool so that when your clients sound as though they are speaking Greek, you can figure out what they're saying.

And in case you're wondering about the title, nude mice do exist.

They're specially bred rodents that are missing their thymus glands. And nude they are; they have no hair or fur on their little rodent bodies.

The first time I came across the term was early in my career when I was editing preclinical study reports for a major pharmaceutical company. I was sure the writer had made a mistake until I looked up *nude mice* in one of my handy-dandy reference books and learned that these little guys are widely used in cancer research. Pretty cool, huh?

The Types of Terms Medical Writers Need To Know

Despite the term *medical* in the phrase *medical writing*, when you work in this field you won't be writing exclusively for medical professionals. Does that surprise you?

Depending on your niche and expertise, in addition to doctors, nurses, and other health care professionals, you might be writing for a lay audience (that's the common person), hospital purchasers, manufacturers and users of medical devices, pharmaceutical sales representatives, members of the insurance industry, or individuals who create and enforce public policy. That's a very broad range, and each of those groups will bring with them a distinct set of terms as well as the associated acronyms and abbreviations. To do your job well, you'll need to have a basic understanding of the language that's unique to each segment. Why? Because the more you know, the more marketable you'll be.

So not only will you need to understand medical terminology, you'll also need a working knowledge of terms related to:

- Health care
- Insurance
- Business and marketing
- Education

You see, medical writing is really not one distinct genre, but one with a very broad scope and multiple components. In my opinion, medical writing falls into 3 broad categories: regulatory, promotional, and educational.

Regulatory writing, a very scientific type of writing, involves translating complex information from clinical trials into technical reports, some of which will be submitted to the federal government. Included here are study protocols, Investigator's Brochures (which are distributed to the scientists who head up clinical trials), patient narratives, and, in some instances, manuscripts detailing the outcomes of clinical trials that will be submitted to medical journals.

Promotional medical writing encompasses any materials created to promote, or sell, a prescription drug, intervention, or medical device. These could be any of the multitudes of sales-training materials (in print and other media) that are used to teach sales representatives about how a new drug or device works and train them to sell it to prescribers. Target audiences for promotional materials are broad, and include the folks who sell the product, those who prescribe it, those who have influence on people who might prescribe it, and those who ultimately will cover the cost, either all or just a portion (third-party payers).

Into the educational category, I lump anything a writer creates for continuing medical education (CME) programs, including writing needs assessments, as well as the content for the actual CME programs. I also consider patient-education materials to be educational writing, since one of their purposes is to educate the consumer and family. I recognize that the ultimate goal of these materials may well be promotional, that is, to educate consumers to the point where they will ask their doctors to prescribe treatment XYZ; however, I classify them as educational, since they differ in style and tone from promotional pieces.

So you can see that the target audiences for whom you could be writing can be quite diverse. And that's why you need to be knowledgeable about more than just medical terms.

Consider for a moment that you're writing website content for a site that will be used by members of the insurance industry. The topic is obesity, and coverage and noncoverage for obesity-related treatments. It's rather obvious that you'll need to become familiar with obesity terms (think BMI, body mass index, and that you'll have to get up to speed on the therapeutic options used to treat the condition (bariatric surgery, for example). However, because you will be putting this information into language that folks in the insurance industry can relate to, you'll also need to be familiar with insurance terms, such as beneficiary, cost-sharing, policy holder, member take-up, disease-management programs, fee-for-service, and so on. You'll probably also need to know about HMOs, PPOs, POS plans, HCFA, and CPT codes.

Here's another scenario. Let's say you're hired to write a few sections of a sales-training program for a new agent that treats children with attention deficit hyperactivity disorder, ADHD, which will soon receive approval from the US Food and Drug Administration (FDA). You're assigned to write an overview of the current marketplace and describe the key competitors of the product. You're expected to discuss market penetration for these agents and include sales figures for the past 5 years. Some terms and acronyms that will likely appear in the background material you'll use to write this section would be formulary, first tier, SWOT, Verispan, ICD codes, and market share.

Since physicians will prescribe this product for children who will likely also have special learning needs, you might need to know educational terms, such as LD, NCLB, and IEP.

Each section (sometimes called a module) of a sales-training program begins with learning objectives (here's where you move even more into that educational realm), so you'll need to know how to write clear and measurable ones. (Hint: "appreciate the benefits of extended-release pain medications" would not be an acceptable learning objective since you can't objectively measure or observe one's appreciation. However, changing the verb from *appreciate* to *identify* or *list* makes the learning objective measurable and observable.) There's also a pretest assessment at the beginning of each module and a posttest assessment at the end, so being able to write test questions is something you'll need to be able to do.

And you thought all you'd need to know were medical terms! Not likely. Before you panic, throw your hands up in despair, and decide that medical writing is not for you, take a deep breath and calm down. You can do this. How do I know? Because I did.

Sure, I had a bit of a science background when I entered the field. Well, at least I had great knowledge of head and neck anatomy, given that I was a speech-language pathologist. Plus I had a basic understanding of health care terms, in particular rehabilitation lingo, since I had worked in hospitals for more than 10 years. But that was it. Once I moved out of familiar therapeutic areas, my knowledge was nil.

How did I get to the point where I was able to understand what I was writing about? I'll let you in on a secret. It was all on-the-job training. I did a lot of asking, reading, and researching when I started out in this field. If someone used an acronym I didn't know, I asked them to define it. If I came across a medical term I didn't know, I cracked open the medical dictionary and committed the definition to memory. I taught myself the meanings of medical suffixes and prefixes so that I could decipher unfamiliar terms. But most important, I surrounded myself with good reference books and developed relationships with experts from whom I could learn.

And you know what? After more than 16 years in this business, I'm still learning. I recently had to question a physician about the abbreviation, EBL. He had added it to a slide deck I was creating with him as part of a CME program. I just could not figure it out given the context in which it appeared. So I wrote him a very nice email and asked him to define it. He was using it to mean *estimated blood loss*. I never would have come up with that. I'm glad I asked.

This book is a great resource for you to have as you prepare yourself for success as a freelance medical writer. Even if you have some medical writing experience under your belt, you'll find this to be a user-friendly reference that will provide you with a good foundation on which to learn more.

In the sections that follow, we'll start off with a brief introduction to medical terminology, and then move into specific medical terms, acronyms, and abbreviations. I devote a lengthy chapter to terms you won't necessarily find in a medical dictionary; they are a combination of medical, health care, insurance, marketing, and writing/publishing terms, such as 510(k), detail aid, and fair balance, to name a few. I've also included chapters on troublesome combinations, body systems, bacterial terminology, Greek letters, and the hierarchy of footnotes. The final section includes a listing of additional useful resources.

That's one of the features of *The Accidental Medical Writer* series. Every book we write has a listing of resources we use frequently. It took us years to find these resources. We include them in our books to save you the time. And because the field of freelance medical writing isn't static, we're finding new resources every day.

Keep in mind that in this book I haven't defined every term you're going to need to know. After all, the 27th edition of *Dorland's Illustrated Medical Dictionary* is 1888 pages long. And that's medical terminology alone. I doubt you'd wade through the book you have in your hand now if it was that lengthy. Always consult a medical dictionary, style guide, or other reference manual when you're unsure of something.

Are you ready? Let's go.

A Medical-Terminology Primer

The complex medical terminology used in medical writing can be frightening for folks who are unfamiliar with the terms. Some aspiring medical writers feel at a disadvantage if they don't have a background in medicine or health care. But you needn't feel intimidated just because you don't come from a science background.

I know some would-be medical writers who believe they need to take a college course or a night class to learn medical terminology. I say save your money. Medical terminology is easy to figure out as long as you take an organized approach and have a great medical dictionary or two and a resource like this book on your bookshelf. Trust me. This isn't brain surgery, although there's a good chance you'll write about brain surgery (in medical terminology that's neurosurgery) at some point in your career.

Understanding the terms is really a matter of realizing that it all goes back to the Greek and Latin origins of the root words. I won't get into a long discussion here about medical etymology (that's the study of word origins) beyond saying that we owe thanks to the Asiatic Greeks and the Italian Greeks for being avid scientists who formed the root words for most of the medical terms we use today. Because these medical terms have common origins, they are easy to decipher once you separate each word into its prefix, root word, combining form, and suffix.

But don't get caught up in whether you should call a syllable or group of syllables a prefix, root word, combining form, or suffix. Those are labels that linguists and etymologists use and, while helpful, you really don't need to categorize these word parts before you can decipher and understand the medical term. I'm not concerned whether you call *tetra–* a prefix or a combining form. (I consider it a prefix when it begins a word, but since it can appear in the middle of words, we can also call it a combining form.) Please don't get hung up on this. What's important is that you recognize that when it appears anywhere in a medical term, it refers to *four*. It's that simple.

In the following sections I'm going to explain some common prefixes, suffixes, and root words and give you some tips that will help you learn how to interpret the medical terms you'll come across as a medical writer.

Keep in mind that the root word will be the building block of the medical term. Think of it as the base of the word. Syllables or groups of syllables are added to the root word either at the end or the beginning to create very precise medical terms. Some terms have more than one root word. Think of these as compound words, just like the familiar ones you use every day: backpack, doorknob, and footstool, to name a few.

Confused? Don't be.

Let's begin at the end.

Medical Suffixes

OK, think back to English class. You should recall that a suffix is a syllable or group of syllables at the end of a word. Medical suffixes follow a very reliable format. For example, the familiar suffix *–ectomy* (as in tonsill*ectomy*) ALWAYS means the surgical removal of an organ or a gland in the body (whether the patient wanted it removed or not). Whenever you see a word with this ending, you can confidently know that a surgeon removed something from the patient. You'll have to examine the prefix of the word to figure out exactly WHAT was removed, though.

You might be wondering why I started with the suffixes first. Well, I think it's important to know how to use medical terms, and to use them correctly, you need to know whether they are nouns, verbs, or adjectives. In medical terminology, the end of a word indicates its part of speech and clues you in to how you should use it. Whenever I find an unfamiliar term, I always decipher it by starting with the ending. I like to know first whether, for example, the word refers to a surgical procedure (a word that ends in *–ectomy* or *–otomy*) or an enzyme (a term ending in *–ase*). Once I know that, then I define the term further. That's why I chose to introduce suffixes first.

But that's just my approach. I would encourage you to use whatever method works best for you. We are all individuals, and we all learn in different ways. Still, regardless of how you approach the task, you'll need to break down terms into prefixes, roots, and suffixes.

What follows are some general medical suffixes with which you should become familiar. Keep in mind that the lists that follow aren't exhaustive. Always refer to a good medical dictionary if you are unsure about the meaning of a word or how you should use it. If all else fails, ASK another medical writer for assistance!

–algia

Every word with this ending refers to pain or some kind of painful condition; for example, **neuralgia** is nerve pain. Any word with this ending will be a noun. Replace the "a" with a "c" (**–algic**) and it becomes an adjective. A variation of this word is the term **analgesic**. The –ic ending tells you it's an adjective, the **–alg** in the middle refers to pain, and the **–an** at the beginning means without. Combine them all together and you have a word pertaining to the absence of pain.

–al

This adjectival suffix simply means pertaining to; for example, **orbital** means pertaining to the orbit (surrounding the eye, not a planet). **Vaginal** means pertaining to the vagina.

–ase

This suffix indicates that the word is some kind of enzyme, such as **amylase**, an enzyme released by the pancreas and the salivary gland. Always a noun.

–blast

You'll find this suffix also used as a prefix. It refers to something in the early stages of growth; for example, a **myeloblast** is an immature cell in the bone marrow. It's a noun until you add an "ic" to the word, making it an adjective, **–blastic**.

–cele

This suffix refers to a hernia or a tumor-like swelling; for example, a **hysterocele** is a hernia of the uterus. A **hydrocele** is a not a hernia, but rather a collection of fluid that results in an outward swelling. Any word with this ending is a noun.

–cide

This form refers to something that kills; for example, a *germicide* is an agent that kills germs. Remove the "e" and add an "al" and it becomes an adjective, *germicidal*, pertaining to an agent that kills germs. As another example, a *spermicidal* agent is one that is capable of killing sperm.

–cusis

A condition related to hearing; for example, *presbycusis* is the age-associated loss of hearing experienced by people as they grow older. Another noun, since it refers to a condition.

–cyte

Related to a cell; for example, a *lymphocyte* is a white blood cell. An *erythrocyte* is a red blood cell. Words with this ending are nouns.

–duct

This suffix means a passage; for example, an *oviduct* is the passage through which a female's egg moves out of the ovary. To change this noun into an adjective, add an "al," *–ductal*, and you have a word that means pertaining to a passage.

–ectasia

Any condition that has to do with stretching or expansion; for example, *telangiectasia* refers to the permanent stretching of certain blood vessels. The "ia" on the end signals you that it's a noun referring to an abnormal condition. Replace the "a" with a "c" and the word becomes an adjective, *–ectasic*.

–ectomy

The surgical removal of an organ, gland, or other element in the body; for example, a ***lumpectomy*** is a removal of a lump, usually containing cancerous tissue, from the breast. An ***appendectomy*** is the surgical removal of the—all together now—appendix. Words with this ending are always nouns.

–emia

Concerning the blood; for example, ***anemia*** is a condition where the body lacks a normal amount of red blood cells. Words with this ending are nouns. Replace the "a" with a "c" and the word becomes an adjective; for example, ***anemic*** means that an individual has a condition in which the body lacks a normal amount of red blood cells. You get the idea. See? I told you it wasn't difficult.

–genesis

I bet you can guess this one. It refers to the beginning, or the origin or development of something; for example, ***pathogenesis*** means the origin of disease. Another noun, but you can create an adjective by removing the "esis" and adding "ic," ***pathogenic***.

–graph

A word that ends with ***–graph*** refers to the instrument used to create a recording or representation; for example, an ***electrocardiograph*** is the instrument that produces a reading of the electrical function of the heart. Again, this suffix indicates a noun.

–graphy

As long as we're talking about the ***–graph*** suffix, let's also mention this one. Words with this ending refer to the act of creating and the study of a writing, recording, or representation of a bodily activity. Using the previous example, ***electromyography*** is the recording and study of the electrical properties of muscles. A noun.

–gram

Words that end with this suffix refer to some type of visual recording or representation of an activity in the body. Taking the previous 2 examples one step further, an *electrocardiogram* is a visual representation of the electrical activity of the heart. A *myelogram* is an x–ray film of the spinal cord. These words will always be nouns.

–ia

This is an extremely common medical suffix that is usually combined with a root word. It refers to any abnormal condition or disease state; for example, *bradycardia* means an abnormally slow heart rate. We've used this suffix before in this section, *–ectasia, –algia*, and in other suffixes that follow.

–itis

This suffix means inflammation. It's that simple. So, *sinusitis* means inflammation of the sinuses. *Phlebitis* is inflammation of a vein. The *–itis* suffix is also used to refer to a condition in which something is inflamed. Again, with either use the word will be a noun.

–lysis

This suffix indicates the destruction or dissolution of something; for example, *electrolysis* is the destruction of excess hair using electric current. Once again, another noun. Be aware that *lysis* is a word when it stands alone. Even in this form, it still means destruction.

–meter

This entry and the one that follows are closely associated. This noun suffix refers to the tool that is used to mechanically examine something; for example, an *audiometer* is the instrument used to examine one's hearing. A *spectrometer* is a tool that measures the index of refraction.

–metry

This is another suffix that refers to the mechanical examination of something; for example, *audiometry* is the examination of one's hearing using an *audiometer*. Another noun, but replace the "y" with an "ic" and the word becomes an adjective.

–oid

Here we have another adjective. In its most simple definition, this suffix means to resemble, or to be like; for example, *lymphoid* means to resemble the lymph tissue. Let's try another. *Osteoid* means resembling bone. You might feel compelled to use words with this ending as nouns, like other words in the English language with this ending, such as asteroid, meteoroid, and so forth. Don't. In medicalese you will always use them as adjectives.

–ology

Simply defined, this means the study of something; for example, *nephrology* is the study of the kidneys and their function. Replace the "y" with an "ist" and you have the specialist who studies something. Thus, a *nephrologist* is the specialist who studies the kidneys and their function. Again, these words will be nouns.

–oma

Words with this ending refer to a tumor, but not necessarily one that is cancerous; for example, a *neuroma* is a tumor that contains nerve cells or fibers, and is not cancerous. A *carcinoma*, however, is a cancerous tumor. And guess what? Another noun.

–opathy

You might be familiar with this suffix. It means an abnormal change, functional disturbance, or disease; for example, *neuropathy* is a general term used to refer to an abnormal change in nerve function. *Myopathy* is an abnormal change in the function of the muscles. Once again, this is another noun that becomes an adjective when you replace the "y" with an "ic."

–opia

This suffix is very similar to the preceding one. It refers also to an abnormal condition, but one that occurs in the eye; for example, *diplopia* is double vision. *Myopia* is near-sightedness. The noun becomes an adjective by replacing the "a" with a "c." This suffix is actually a combination of a root word, *op*, which refers to the eye, and the suffix, *–ia*, which, as you learned earlier, refers to an abnormal condition.

–osis

This is another suffix that usually refers to an abnormal condition; for example, *polyposis* indicates a condition in which the patient has abnormal development of polyps. Once again, this is a noun.

–ostomy

This suffix and the following one are very similar and easy to confuse. *–ostomy* refers to a surgical procedure that creates an artificial opening; for example, a *colostomy* is a surgery that creates an opening between the colon and the surface of the body. These words are nouns.

–otomy

Any word ending in *–otomy* is a procedure that cuts into something; for example, a *craniotomy* is a surgical procedure that cuts into the skull. You can't interchange this with *–ectomy*, though. The same goes for *–ostomy*. An *–otomy* cuts, but an *–ectomy* both cuts AND removes, whereas an *–ostomy* cuts so that an artificial opening can be created. Don't mix up these suffixes. Another noun.

–penia

This refers to not enough of something; for example, *osteopenia* means reduced bone mass, or literally too little bone. Are you sensing a pattern here? The *–ia* suffix creates nouns, but as you've seen often enough, the *–ic* suffix makes the word an adjective. So an *osteopenic* woman is one who has reduced bone mass.

–plasia

The most common meaning of this suffix is abnormal or excessive growth; for example, *dysplasia* is a term that means abnormal development of the cells. You can make this noun an adjective by replacing the "ia" with a "tic," *dysplastic*.

–plasty

This suffix refers to a surgical procedure that repairs or reconstructs a part of the body; for example, a *rhinoplasty* is, quite frankly, a nose job. A *septoplasty* is the repair of a deviated septum. Another noun.

–plegia

You're probably familiar with this suffix. It means paralysis; for example, *hemiplegia* means the condition where one side of the body is paralyzed. This is another noun. To create the adjective form, replace the "a" with a "c." Thus, a *hemiplegic* man is one who has paralysis on only one side of his body.

–plexy

This suffix refers to an abrupt or sudden attack, such as a stroke or a seizure; for example, *cataplexy* means a sudden episode of weak muscles. This noun form becomes an adjective by removing the "y" and adding "ic," *cataplexic.*

—rrhagia

This refers to an abnormal or excessive discharge; for example, *menorrhagia* means heavy menstrual bleeding. Like many of the suffixes you've seen before, you can make this noun into a verb by replacing the "a" with a "c." So, a *menorrhagic* woman is one who has a heavy period. Let's take this one step further and introduce the term *hemorrhagic*. There's that suffix again. It means pertaining to excessive bleeding or hemorrhage.

—rrhea

Not to be confused with the previous entry, this suffix literally means flowing. It usually refers to excess flowing or excess production of something; for example, *diarrhea* means excess discharge of fluid matter from the bowel. *Seborrhea* refers to the production of too much sebum. However, the word *menorrhea* means menstrual bleeding, or flow, usually too much, but not always. This suffix has the potential to confuse even the most careful writers.

—sclerosis

In this context it means hardening; for example, *atherosclerosis* is a hardening of the lining of the arteries. The adjective form would be *–sclerotic*. If a woman has *atherosclerosis*, her arteries would be *atherosclerotic*. This suffix is actually a combination of a root word, *scler*, which means hardening, and the suffix *–osis*. The *–osis* at the end clues you in that this is an abnormal condition.

—scope

A word that ends with *–scope* refers to a tool used for viewing something. The root word indicates the type of tool; for example, a *laryngoscope* is an instrument used to view the larynx, either during an examination or during surgery. Another noun, but it becomes an adjective when you remove the "e" and add "ic." So a *laryngoscopic* procedure would be one that was performed using a ***laryngoscope***. Another variation of this suffix is the noun form, ***–scopy***, which refers to the visual examination itself. So a ***laryngoscopy*** is the visual examination of the larynx using a ***laryngoscope***.

–trophy

This suffix pertains to growth and development; for example, ***hypertrophy*** is too much growth or an overgrowth. Once again, you can create the adjective form by removing the "y" and adding "ic," ***hypertrophic***.

Medical Prefixes

Now that you've familiarized yourself with some medical endings, let's move on to prefixes. A prefix is a syllable or a group of syllables at the beginning of a medical term that gives you additional information about its meaning. It might indicate direction, quantity, size, or location.

Before I discuss meanings, I need to say a word about usage here. The most common prefixes used in medical terminology are most always joined to a root word WITHOUT using a hyphen. Novice medical writers frequently don't follow this convention; however, if you consistently write anti-microbial or co-author, the editor who reviews your work is going to get a little cranky. The correct forms of these words (at least in medical writing) are antimicrobial or coauthor. Take my word for it.

And please don't rely on your word-processing program's spell-check function to determine whether you've spelled these words correctly. I'm using Microsoft® Office® Word to write this book and the incorrectly hyphenated words in the previous paragraph appear to be absolutely correct, proving that even folks who develop such software aren't aware of all the grammar rules that exist.

But that's not to say that all prefixes connect without a hyphen. Some prefixes ALWAYS are hyphenated, such as self- (self-reported, self-mutilation, but not selfish), quasi- (quasi-experimental), and cross- (cross-reactive). Still, exceptions exist. If you are unsure whether or not to insert a hyphen, consult one of these references:

- The latest edition of the *American Medical Association (AMA)*

Manual of Style
- *Merriam-Webster's Collegiate® Dictionary*, or a similar English dictionary
- *Dorland's Illustrated Medical Dictionary*, or a similar medical dictionary

Keep in mind that the clients for whom you will be writing may have very unique style guidelines they want you to follow. So even though the AMA style guide advocates a particular style, your clients may choose to ignore it and develop their own editorial styles to suit their particular needs. Whenever you begin a project, it's always a good idea to check with your clients to see if they have a style guide or certain conventions they want you to follow. Doing this at the beginning of a project will save you headaches later.

You'll find other books that discuss grammar usage (including rules for hyphenation) in the resources section at the end of this book.

Getting back to the subject of spell-check software, I need to mention one more thing. The spell-check function that is part of your word-processing program is not designed to check the spelling of complex medical terms. To accurately check the spelling of your work, you might want to consider installing a medical terminology spell-check program that complements your existing spell-check function.

Several programs are available. Just go to your favorite search engine and type in "*spell check software for medical terminology.*" You can obtain some of these programs as free downloads; others you can purchase for relatively low prices, say, around $30, but some can be pricey (around $200 or more). I'm cautious about downloading free programs, and so should you. I won't recommend one program over another, but make sure the software you choose is compatible with your computer operating system AND includes a large number of entries. Customer support is another issue to consider.

a–, an–

This is a very common prefix. It simply means without, or not, depending on the context; for example, ***anencephaly*** is a condition in which the brain is absent; literally, the individual is born without a brain. As another example, ***asexual*** means not sexual.

ab–

It means to subtract or move away from. So, when a physical therapist says that a person can't ***abduct*** the upper extremities, it means the individual has difficulty lifting the arms upward when the limbs are initially placed at the sides of the body. Don't confuse this prefix with the next one.

ad–

The ***ad–*** prefix means the opposite of the previous one. It means to increase, move toward, or bring together (think of the arithmetic term, add). Using the previous example, ***adduction*** then would mean to bring the limbs toward the body from an initial raised position.

ambi–

This means both; for example, a person who is ***ambidextrous*** is one who can use both hands equally well.

ante–

This prefix means before or in front of; for example, an ***antecedent*** event is one that comes before. We use this prefix in plain old English words, too. Ever hear of the word ***antebellum***? It means before the war. Some writers have a tendency to use this prefix to mean after, so be cautious when interpreting or using terms with this prefix.

ant–, anti–

Either form of this prefix means against, opposite, or preventive; for example, an **antihypertensive** agent is one that prevents (or controls) high blood pressure. A more literal interpretation would be to say that it works against elevated blood pressure. An **antifungal** drug is a medication used to eliminate fungal infections. It works against the fungus. This is another prefix in common everyday usage.

apo–

This prefix refers to a separation or, in some cases, a derivation; for example, **apomorphine** is a compound that is derived from morphine.

bi–, bis–

Both forms mean two, both, twice, or double, depending on the context; for example, **binocular** vision means to see with both (two) eyes simultaneously.

brachy–

This combining form means short; for example, **brachycephaly** is a condition in which an individual's head is abnormally short. Make sure you don't confuse this form with the next entry. They sound similar, particularly if a speaker talks quickly and you're not familiar with the context of the conversation.

brady–

Another combining form, this term means slow; for example, **bradycardia** refers to an abnormally slow heartbeat.

cat–, cata–

This prefix has 2 meanings. One is directional, meaning downward. The other implies something negative. We used this prefix in a previous example, **cataplexy**. In that context, it implied something negative. But **cataphoria** refers to a permanent downward gazing of the eyes.

circum–

This prefix means around or in a circular motion; for example, **circumarticular** means around a joint. This is a prefix that's used outside of the medical realm, too. **Circumnavigate** is one term that comes to mind. It means to travel around the world.

co–, col–, com–, con–

The ending letter of this prefix changes depending on the alphabet letter that follows. Still, no matter what form, these prefixes mean with or together; for example, a **concomitant** illness is one that a patient has at the same time as another illness. Likewise, a **concomitant** medication is a drug that a patient takes while using other medications. It does not mean the drugs are consumed simultaneously; rather, the patient has prescriptions for 2 different agents and is supposed to take both drugs as indicated on the label.

contra–

This prefix means against or opposed to; for example, a **contraindication** is a condition, such as an allergy, that prevents a patient from taking a certain medication or engaging in a specific activity. Being allergic to iodide is a **contraindication** to taking potassium iodide pills in the event of a nuclear emergency.

de–

This prefix is another with a negative implication. It can signify a loss, removal, reversal, privation, or cessation; for example, **decalcify** means to remove calcium salts. **Detoxify** means to remove toxic substances from one's body.

di–

Another prefix indicating quantity, *di–* refers to two, twice, or double depending on the context; for example, *diplopia* (an example we used in the suffix section) means double vision.

dis–

Another prefix denoting something negative, *dis–* implies a loss or absence of something. In certain contexts it can also mean a separation or moving apart; for example, *disorder* means the absence of order. *Displacement* is the loss of a normal anatomic position, but *dissociation* means the act of separating something.

dys–

Don't confuse this prefix with the previous entry, even though this one also has a negative implication. *Dys–* means difficult or painful. It can also mean abnormal; for example, *dystonia* means abnormal muscle tone.

ect–, ecto–

Both forms refer to outer or outside of; for example, *ectocytic* pertains to something that is outside of the cell.

en– (em– before certain letters)

The *en–* prefix changes to *em–* when it precedes the letters "b," "p," or "ph." It means in or on; for example, *encephalopathy* refers to a disease in the brain (literally, inside the head, since *celphalo* is the root word for head).

endo–, ento–

Both forms of this prefix refer to inner or within; for example, the *endocardium* is the innermost layer of the heart. The *entoderm* is the innermost germ layer of an embryo.

epi–

Another prefix denoting placement, this one means above or beside. In some contexts it means upon; for example, the *epicanthus* is the vertical fold of skin beside the eye on either side of the nose.

ex–, exo–

A common medical prefix, it means outside of or away from, in some contexts, without; for example, *exotropia* is a condition in which the eyes turn away from each other. *Exencephaly* is a condition in which the brain lies outside of the skull.

hemi–

We used this prefix before when discussing the term *hemiplegia*. The prefix means one-half; for example, *hemiplegia* is a paralysis in one-half of the body.

hyper–

Another common medical prefix, it means above normal, excessive, elevated, or increased; for example, *hypertension* means above-normal blood pressure. *Hyperactivity* means excessive activity.

hypo–

The opposite of *hyper–*, this prefix means below normal or decreased; for example, using the previous example of blood pressure, *hypotension* means below-normal blood pressure.

il–, im–, in–, ir–

All forms mean not; whether to use the "I" or one of the other ending letters depends on the alphabetic letter that follows the prefix. Another meaning is in or into. For example, *irregular* means not regular. *Illogical* means not logical.

infra–

This prefix refers to below; for example, *inframandibular* means below the bottom jaw.

inter–

This prefix means between; for example, *intercapillary* means between the capillaries.

intra–

Not to be confused with the preceding prefix, this one means within; for example, *intra-articular* means within the joint. Don't get *inter–* and *intra–* confused. You might be wondering why I put a hyphen between *intra–* and the root word *articular* when I told you earlier that prefixes are usually joined to root words without hyphens. Well, common rules of usage call for a hyphen when certain repeating letters appear. Since we would have two "a's" side by side, we insert a hyphen to prevent any confusion. If the word was *intrahepatic*, meaning within the liver, no hyphen would be necessary.

intro–

Here is another prefix that means in or into; for example, an *introitus* is a term for an entrance into a cavity or space. You can remember this by thinking of the word *introduction*, a lead-in to something.

macro–

This term means large; for example, *macroglossia* is a condition in which the person's tongue is abnormally large.

mesi–, mesio–, meso–

These forms pertain to the middle; for example, *mesocardia* refers to a condition in which the heart is abnormally located near the middle line of the chest. Whether to use the "i" or the "io" depends on the alphabet letter that follows the prefix.

micro–

You can probably guess the meaning of this prefix. It means small; for example, a *microscope* is a tool for viewing small items. *Microvasculature* refers to the finer blood vessels in the body.

mon–, mono–

Both forms mean one or single; for example, *monocular* is an adjective that refers to using only one eye. A *monocyte* is a blood cell that has only one nucleus.

multi–

Another common medical prefix, this one means many or much; for example, *multiarticular* is an adjective that refers to something that affects many joints.

neo–

This prefix means new; for example, a *neonate* is a newborn baby. No, it doesn't just refer to Keanu Reeves' character in the film *The Matrix*.

para–

This prefix means beside or near; another meaning is abnormal. For example, *paracardiac* refers to beside the heart, whereas *paragraphia* is a condition in which the individual writes abnormally. However, it's also used in the term *paraplegia*. In this context it means paralysis of the legs and lower portion of the body.

peri–

This prefix means around; for example, the *pericardium* is the sac that surrounds the heart.

poly–

This prefix means many or much; for example, ***polymenorrhea*** (remember the suffix ***–rrhea***? It means flowing) means abnormally frequent menstruation.

post–

A very common medical prefix, it means after (as in time) or behind (as in location); for example, ***postmenopausal*** means after menopause (the cessation of menstruation). ***Postnasal*** mean occurring behind the nose.

pre–

Another medical prefix you'll encounter often, this one means before; for example, ***prenatal*** care is care an expectant mother receives before birth.

pro–

This prefix means coming before or in front of; for example, a ***prodrug*** is simply a precursor of a drug. It must undergo some type of transformation before becoming the active drug.

pseudo–

This form means fake or false; for example, ***pseudoangina*** is a condition resembling true angina pectoris (sudden chest pain), but without evidence of any heart disease.

re–

This prefix means again, or to go back, or return to a previous state; for example, ***reabsorb*** means to absorb again.

retro–

This prefix means backward or behind; for example, ***retrocervical*** means behind the cervix.

semi–

This prefix is similar to **hemi–**. It, too, means one-half, but it also means partial; for example, a **semicoma** is a partial coma, more like a stupor.

sub–

This prefix means under or below. In some contexts it means less than normal; for example, **substandard** treatment is care that is less than the normally expected standard of care. **Subcutaneous**, however, means under the skin.

super–

This prefix can mean above (as in location) or excessive (more than normal); for example, a **superinfection** is one that is more severe than normal. **Superdistension** refers to excessive distension or stretching. Notice that the prefix, which can stand alone and still have meaning, is attached to the root word without a hyphen.

supra–

Not to be confused with **super–**, this prefix refers exclusively to location. It means above; for example, **supraclavicular** means located above the clavicle.

syn–

This prefix refers to a union or some type of association; for example, **synchilia** is a condition in which the lips are congenitally fused together.

tetra–

This prefix, which some consider a combining form, means 4; for example, **tetradactyly** is a condition in which an individual has only 4 digits on a hand or foot.

trans–

This prefix means through or across; for example, when a surgeon makes a *transabdominal* incision, he or she makes it through the abdominal wall.

tri–

Another prefix indicating number, *tri–* refers to 3; for example, *trisomy* is a condition in which an extra chromosome is present in a cell that otherwise would have only 2 chromosomes.

uni–

This prefix also refers to number. It means one or single; for example, a *unicellular* organism is one made up of a single cell.

Root Words

The final element of medical terms you need to be familiar with is the root word. Think of the root word as the foundation of a medical term. You've already learned that the suffix tells you the part of speech and how the term is to be used; the prefix clarifies the meaning of the term, often indicating direction, location, or quantity. Now you can look at the root word to decipher exactly what the term means. Root words often indicate a part of the body, or they might refer to a particular compound, substance, or property.

For the first few terms that follow, I'll break them down into the component parts so that you can see how they were created.

abdomin, abdomino

As you can probably figure out, this root word refers to the abdomen. Let's use a previous example, *transabdominal*, and break it down into its distinct elements. The prefix *trans–* as you learned before means through or across. So *transabdominal* is a combination of a prefix *trans–*, the root word *abdomin*, and the suffix *–al*, meaning pertaining to. The suffix makes the term an adjective. Thus, the term means pertaining to through the abdomen, and you might use it to refer to a type of incision, a *transabdominal* incision, for example.

Now I want to make sure you're clear on this. Root words don't have to appear at the end of a term. They can come at the beginning, middle, or end. Let's review another example. *Abdominoscopy* is a combination of the root word *abdomino* and the suffix *–scopy*. You learned earlier that this suffix refers to a visual examination using some kind of instrumentation. So, the term means an examination of the abdominal cavity with a tool, perhaps a laparoscope.

If you engage in this exercise whenever you come across unfamiliar medical terms, you should be able to figure them out. That's not to say some words still won't trip you up. Some rather complex terminology flies around in this industry, so keep your medical dictionary handy.

aden, adeno

This root word refers to a gland; for example, ***adenoma*** is a tumor that forms in a glandular structure. It's a combination of the root word ***aden*** and the suffix ***–oma***, which, as you learned earlier, means tumor.

aer, aero

This refers to air, and in some contexts, gas; for example, ***aeropathy*** refers to any abnormal condition caused by changes in atmospheric pressure, such as decompression sickness. As you can see, it's a combination of the root word ***aero*** and the suffix ***–opathy***, meaning an abnormal change or condition.

andro

This form refers to masculine; for example, an ***androcyte*** is a male sex cell since the suffix ***–cyte*** refers to cell.

angi, angio

This root generally refers to the blood vessels; for example, ***angiopathy*** is a general term that refers to a disease of the vessels. There's that suffix ***–opathy*** again.

arter, arterio

This root refers to the arteries; for example, ***arteriosclerosis*** is a disease in which the arterial walls thicken and lose their elasticity. It combines the root word ***arterio*** with the suffix ***–sclerosis***.

artic, articul

Both forms of this root word pertain to the joints; for example, *disarticulation* refers to a separation of a joint.

astro

This form indicates a relationship to a star; for example, an *astrocytoma* is a tumor made up of *astrocytes*, very specific cells that, for want of a better description, are shaped like stars.

bio

If you think back to your high-school years, you should recall that *biology* class was the study of life. So, *bio* refers to life.

bronch, bronchi, broncho

This root word refers to the air passages within the lungs, known as the bronchial tubes. So *bronchoscopy* is the visual examination of these air passages using, as you might guess, a *bronchoscope*.

carcin, carcino

This root refers to any form of cancer; for example, an *adenocarcinoma* is a cancerous tumor that develops in glandular tissue or in a glandular structure. This term is a combination of 2 root words, *adeno* and *carcin*, followed by the suffix *–oma*.

cardi, cardio

Both forms of this root word refer to the heart; for example, *echocardiography* is a method of graphically recording the movement of the internal structure of the heart.

cephal, cephalo

This term refers to the head; for example, *encephalopathy*, which combines the prefix *en–*, the root word *cephalo* and the suffix

–opathy, refers to any disease of the brain (literally, inside the head). We used this example before when discussing the prefix *en–*. *Cephalopathy*, on the other hand, pertains to a disease of the head. Understand the difference?

chro, chrom, chromo

These forms refer to color; for example, *monochromatic* means pertaining to a single color.

cyst, cysti, cysto

These root forms pertain to a cyst or, in some contexts, the bladder; for example, *nephrocystitis* refers to an inflammation in the kidneys and bladder. This is a compound term that combines 2 root words, *nephro* (which refers to the kidneys) and *cyst* with a suffix, *–itis*.

cyt, cyto

These are additional forms that you could confuse with the previous entries. They refer to the cell. Going back to a previous example, *astrocytoma* is another compound medical term. It combines the roots *astro* and *cyt* with the suffix *–oma*. It refers to a tumor made up of star-like cells.

dacry

If you write extensively in the field of ophthalmology, you'll frequently come across words with this root form. It pertains to tears; for example, the term *dacryogenic* pertains to anything that promotes the secretion of tears. The suffix is the adjectival form of *–genesis*.

dacty, dactyl

I used this root before when I defined *tetradactyly*. It pertains to the digits, usually fingers, but can also refer to the toes. Another example, *clinodactyly*, refers to a permanent condition in which one or more fingers deviate laterally or medially.

dent, denti, dento

Do I even need to explain the forms of this root word? Yes, they refer to the teeth; for example, *dentition* pertains to the natural teeth (as opposed to false teeth) in their natural position in the mouth.

derm, derma, dermat, dermato, dermo

All forms of this root word refer to the skin; for example, a *dermatologist* is the specialist who treats disorders of the skin.

gastr, gastro

These forms pertain to the stomach; for example, *gastritis* means the inflammation of the stomach.

gloss

This root word refers to the tongue; for example, a *glossectomy* is a procedure in which the tongue is removed.

gluc, gluco, glucos, glyc, glyco

These forms pertain generally to sugar and more specifically to glucose; for example, *glucosuria* refers to glucose that is detected in the urine.

graph

I already explained this form when it appears at the end of medical terms. In that context, it refers to the instrument that creates a visual representation of a body function. But I also want to include it here in the section on root words. In this context, it pertains to writing, for example, *macrographia* is a condition in which a person writes using abnormally large letters.

gyn, gyne, gyneco, gyno

These root forms pertain to a woman or female; for example, a *gynecologist* is the specialist who treats diseases of women.

hem, hema, hemat, hemato

These forms refer to blood; for example, a *hematologist* is the specialist who treats individuals with diseases of the blood.

hepat, hepatico, hepato

These forms pertain to the liver; for example, *hepatitis* refers to an inflammation of the liver.

hydr, hydro

These roots refer to water or fluid; for example, *anhydrous* means deprived of water. It combines the prefix *an–* with the root word and an adjectival suffix.

hyster, hystero

These forms refer to the uterus; for example, a *hysterectomy* is the removal of the uterus.

kines, kinesio

These forms pertain to movement; for example, *hyperkinesia* refers to abnormally increased movement.

latero, lateral

I couldn't decide whether to identify these forms as prefixes or root words. Where I categorize them isn't important. Just remember that they mean to one side. Here are 2 examples of their use. *Mediolateral* means to the middle and off to one side. *Lateroversion* means to be turned to one side.

leuk, leuko (also leuc, leuco)

The forms of this root word mean white; for example, *leukodystrophy* is an abnormal condition that affects the white substance of the brain.

lith, litho

These forms refer to stone; for example, *lithotripsy* is a procedure used to disintegrate stones found in certain organs of the body, for example, the upper urinary tract.

mal

This term means inadequate, incomplete, or imperfect; for example, *maladjustment* refers to an inadequate adjustment to the environment.

malac, malaco

These forms pertain to soft or a softening; for example, *osteomalacia* is a disease in which the bones in the body begin to soften.

mega, megal, megalo

These forms mean extra large; for example, *cardiomegaly* refers to an enlarged heart.

melan, melano

These forms pertain to black or dark pigmentation; for example, *melanism* is a condition (usually genetic) in which the skin is excessively pigmented or black.

meno

This form refers to menstruation. As you learned in an earlier example, *menorrhea* is a term used to describe menstruation.

myo

This form pertains to the muscles; for example, *electromyography* is the electrical examination of an individual's muscle movements.

naso

This root word refers to the nose; for example, a *nasogastric* tube is a feeding tube that runs through the nose into the stomach.

nephr, nephro

These forms refer to the kidney; for example, a *nephrectomy* is the surgical procedure that removes the kidney.

neur, neuro

These root forms refer to the nerves and the nervous system; for example, *neuralgia* indicates nerve pain.

ocul, oculo

These roots pertain to the eye. Using a previous example, *monocular* pertains to only one eye.

odyn, odyno

These forms refer to pain or distress; for example, *gastrodynia* is an old-fashioned stomach ache.

olig, oligo

These forms refer to scanty or too little; for example, *oligomenorrhea* means infrequent menstruation and/or diminished menstrual flow.

ost, oste, osteo

These forms pertain to bone; for example, *osteoporosis* is a condition in which the bones lose mass and can become fractured easily.

path, patho, pathy

These forms pertain to disease or sickness; for example, a **psychopath** refers to person who suffers from a very specific mental (psychological) disturbance.

phob

This root word refers to fear; for example, **arachnophobia** is a fear of spiders.

pneum, pneuma, pneumat, pneumato, pneumo

These forms refer to air, the lungs, or the act of breathing; for example, a **pneumothorax** is an abnormal condition in which air accumulates in the space around the lungs.

presby

This form refers to old age or aging; for example, **presbyopia** is a very specific vision impairment that develops as we age.

psych, psycho

These forms pertain to the mind; for example, **psychosis** refers to a disorder of the mind.

pyo

This form relates to pus; for example, a **pyocyst** is a cyst that is filled with pus.

rhin, rhino

These forms refer to the nose; for example, **rhinitis** is inflammation of the mucous membranes of the nose; in essence, a cold.

sarc, sarco

These forms refer to flesh or tissue; for example, a *sarcoma* is a tumor composed of connective tissue.

spasm

This form refers to involuntary muscle contractions; for example, a *hysterospasm* is an involuntary muscle contraction in the uterus.

steno

This form refers to a narrowing or constriction; for example, *stenosis* is a term used to describe a condition in which a passageway or a duct is abnormally narrow.

therm, thermo

These forms pertain to heat or temperature; for example, *hypothermia* is a condition in which the internal temperature of the body drops to dangerously low levels.

throm, thrombo

These forms refer to a blood clot or the process of clotting; for example, a *thrombocytopenia* is an abnormal condition in which the number of blood platelets is decreased and the body's ability to clot is diminished.

tox, toxic, toxico, toxo

These forms refer to poison; for example, *toxicoid* pertains to any substance that resembles a poison. *Toxicosis* is any condition that is caused by a poison.

ur, uri

Although these are not technically root words, I do want to discuss them here. They pertain to *urine*.

vas, vasculo, vaso

These forms pertain to the blood vessels; for example, **vasoactive** refers to something that has an effect on the size of the blood vessels.

A Few Confusing Combos

I f you read my story in *The Accidental Medical Writer*, you know that I've been in this business for a long time, more than 16 years. During that time, I've seen a lot of poor writing and, I confess, I'm responsible for some of it. At least in my early years, I made quite a few mistakes. Don't get me wrong. I still make mistakes today, but when I look back at some of the material I wrote during my first year of freelance medical writing, I cringe. I'm not alone, though. Some of my colleagues tell me that they do the same thing.

The point I want to make here is that every writer makes mistakes. Beginning writers tend to make more mistakes than experienced ones; however, one caveat applies. The best writers learn from those mistakes and avoid making them in the future. Mediocre writers—even those with experience—make the same errors over and over again, without remorse.

In this section, I'm going to discuss certain words that are troublesome for medical writers, even those with a few years of experience under their belt. The terms that follow are ones I've seen writers stumble over time and time again.

adverse/averse

These terms are adjectives with completely different meanings. *Adverse* means unfavorable. In medicalese it is often paired with the words *event* or *effect*, as in an *adverse event* or an *adverse effect*, to describe an unfavorable condition that arose as the result of medical treatment. *Averse*, in contrast, means opposed to, as in the sentence, "The patient was *averse* to taking the study medication on schedule."

affect/effect

It drives me crazy when writers use these terms incorrectly. Although both terms can be used either as a noun or a verb, it is more common to use **affect** as the verb and **effect** as the noun. Here are some examples: "The drug **affected** the patient's equilibrium," meaning that it altered or changed the person's balance. In this sentence, **affect** is the verb.

"One **effect** of the drug was dizziness," meaning that dizziness was a consequence of taking the drug. In this sentence, **effect** is the noun.

How can you keep them straight? I use a reverse correlation and remember that the v*E*rb form, **affect**, does not begin with an "e."

Now let me point out that when used as a noun, **affect** refers to a person's demeanor or emotional range, as in, "He has a flat **affect**," meaning he shows little emotion. When used as a verb, **effect** means to make something happen, as in, "She **effected** change in her neighborhood by promoting personal responsibility." She was the catalyst that created some kind of neighborhood change.

autopsy/necropsy

These two terms confused me greatly when I began my medical writing career. For some reason, I believed that an **autopsy** was an examination of a dead human and a **necropsy** was an examination of a dead animal. Wrong! Well, maybe I wasn't so wrong after all.

According to my medical dictionary, both of these terms refer to an examination of a body after death. Occasionally you'll find them used synonymously; however, in common usage **autopsy** is more often applied to humans and **necropsy** reserved for animals, but not always.

callous/callus

You know that hard, thick skin hanging out on the sole of your foot? It's called a *callus*. Refrain from inserting an "o" when you're using this term as a noun. But if you want to talk about a *callous* individual, that is, one who has little regard for people's feelings, then, by all means, please correctly add the "o."

This is one of those errors your spell-check software rarely picks up, so be very careful when proofing your draft.

complement/compliment

Regardless of the industry in which you write, you need to know the difference between these terms. *Complement* means to add to or supplement; for example, "The slide show *complemented* the doctor's lecture."

In contrast, a *compliment* is a favorable comment, as in, "He gave the nurse a *compliment* when he praised her for the care she gave to his mother." In another context, *complimentary* materials are those that are given freely at no charge.

compose/comprise

These terms, which are not exclusive to the medical industry, still trip up even experienced medical writers. To understand how to use them, consider the whole versus the parts. The whole *comprises* (or includes) the parts, but the whole is *composed of* the parts; for example, "The study population *comprises* 2 groups: healthy volunteers and subjects with hypertension." You could write this another way: "The study population is *composed* of 2 groups: healthy volunteers and subjects with hypertension."

creatine/creatinine

I wish I would have known these were 2 different substances

when I was starting my career as a freelance medical writer. They are very different, but your spell-check program won't pick up when you've used them incorrectly.

Creatine is an acid that occurs naturally in the body. It supplies energy to muscles and nerves. *Creatine* supplementation has been suggested as a possible treatment for certain medical conditions (and as a way to build muscles), but its use is somewhat controversial.

Creatinine is a metabolic byproduct that is filtered through the kidneys. If the kidneys aren't functioning properly, *creatinine* levels in the blood and urine will rise. That's why doctors measure something called *creatinine* clearance as an indicator of how well the kidneys are functioning.

disc/disk

Whether you spell this term with a "c" or a "k" depends on the context. I'm going to defer to the *AMA Manual of Style, 10th Edition*, for this one. According to this reference, use a "c" when you're referring to ophthalmologic terms, such as the optic *disc*. If you're referring to any other anatomical term, use a "k," such as when talking about lumbar *disks*. So when you're writing about a procedure that surgically removes part of the lumbar *disks*, it's a *diskectomy*, not a discectomy.

If you're writing about computers, use *disk* to talk about the disk drive. When you're talking about a compact *disc* or a video *disc*, use the "c."

discreet/discrete

Another very confusing combo, these terms are often used interchangeably, even though they have different meanings. *Discreet* is an adjective that pertains to the act of discretion. It means one is sensible and controlled, as in, "She was *discreet* in her approach to the matter of the patient's sexual preference." You probably won't use this term very often in medical writing.

On the other hand, you might have occasion to use the term **discrete**. It means distinct, perhaps having unique characteristics, as in, "The tumor was made up of **discrete** cells."

dose/dosage

I'll admit these words are easy to confuse. Here's the easiest way I can think of to explain how you should use them. The term **dose** refers to an amount that is given at 1 time; the term **dosage** refers to the schedule of the administration of the drug: "The recommended **dosage** is 1000 mg/day for 14 days, given as 2 divided **doses** of 500 mg."

efficacy/effectiveness

The first time I heard the word **efficacy** was when I was in graduate school working as a graduate assistant for a professor. He had a penchant for the word. My job was to transcribe his lectures (from a Dictaphone®, so I'm dating myself). Instead of **efficacy,** I heard and typed **ethicacy**, even though it didn't fit into the context, and it wasn't even a real word. After I mistyped the term more than a few times, he flatly told me that if I wanted to work in a clinical field, I needed to learn how to spell the word correctly and understand its meaning. Thank you, Dr. Kruse.

Efficacy means the power to produce an expected result. When investigators conduct a clinical trial, among other outcomes they examine the **efficacy** of a drug, device, intervention, or treatment regimen. They want to know whether the agent being studied has the power to produce the effect they are expecting.

Effectiveness, on the other hand, generally is a measure of the accuracy or success of a device or treatment. Granted, in some dictionaries it has the same definition as ***efficacy***; some experts even assert that you can use these terms interchangeably. I respectfully disagree, and here's why.

Let's consider a new medication that's expected to reduce blood pressure (BP), and let's say during the clinical studies the investigators expected it to reduce BP by an average of 30%, and it did—during the clinical trial under very controlled situations. Now that folks are using the drug in real-life situations, however, and not in the controlled clinical environment, the agent reduces BP by, on average, only 15%.

So, did the drug have the power to produce the expected outcome (***efficacy***)? Sure, during the clinical trial. Does it have the same effect in real life? No it doesn't, although it still is ***effective*** in reducing blood pressure. So the distinction becomes the drug's performance during the clinical trial versus its performance in real life.

This isn't just my take, however. When I was writing an early draft of this book, I was curious about how other medical writers interpreted ***efficacy*** and ***effectiveness***. So I posted the question to a listserv for freelance writers, and 90% of those who responded had similar definitions.

fewer/less

These terms are not interchangeable, no matter what your best friend tells you. Here's a quick lesson. Use ***fewer*** when referring to a particular number of something, that is, an amount you can count: "***Fewer*** patients took their medications as prescribed." Use ***less*** when making comparisons about volume, degree, or value: "Despite regular deposits my SEP IRA is worth ***less*** money today than a year ago."

idiopathic/iatrogenic

You'll come across these terms often, so it's important to learn their meanings. *Idiopathic* means to have no apparent cause or etiology, so *idiopathic* pulmonary fibrosis is a lung disease for which no apparent cause can be found.

Iatrogenic means the result of a health care intervention, and it's usually not a good thing. For example, an *iatrogenic* injury might occur when the surgeon accidentally nicks the patient's bowel during surgery, or when a patient receives the wrong medication or the wrong dose.

incidence/prevalence

These two words are commonly used in medical writing when writing about epidemiology and they are easy to confuse. I know veteran medical writers who need to check on the meaning of these terms whenever they use them.

Incidence is the number of new cases of a certain condition in a specified time period, usually a year. So, if the annual *incidence* of pancreatic cancer in the United States is 38,000, this means that 38,000 people will be newly diagnosed with the disease each year.

Prevalence is the total number of people overall who have a certain condition. Using a heart disease example, if you read that the *prevalence* of cardiovascular disease in the United States is around 61 million, this means that 61 million people in the United States are walking around with heart disease. It does not mean that 61 million people will be diagnosed with heart disease this year.

in vivo/in vitro

If you come to medical writing from a nonscientific field (without any recall of Latin from your high-school years), you may unintentionally interchange the meanings of these terms. Yes, they are Latin. The first, *in vivo*, means within the body; the second, *in vitro*, means in an artificial environment outside of the body. Thus, *in vitro* fertilization is fertilization of the egg by the sperm in a test tube (Petri dish is probably more accurate). When you read that a drug was tested *in vivo* it means that it was tested within a body (not necessarily a human one, though).

ligate/litigate

I guarantee the first time you come across the word *ligate* you'll think it's a mistake. Even your spell-check software will identify it as an error, unless you've installed special medical spell-check software as I discussed earlier. *Ligate* means to tie off or bind, as in "To reduce blood loss, the surgeon will *ligate* the blood vessel."

Litigate means to pursue a lawsuit, as in "He assigned his up-and-coming attorney to litigate the case against the chemical company who dumped toxic waste in Love Canal."

mucous/mucus

Oh, if only the English language were simple and straightforward. Unfortunately, it's not, as this confusing combo shows. Although both terms refer to the same substance, *mucus* is the noun and *mucous* is the adjective. "The patient's nose is filled with *mucus* and the *mucous* membranes of the upper respiratory tract are inflamed."

parental/parenteral

These terms are not easy to confuse from the standpoint of their meanings. They are, however, very similar in spelling. When you're in a rush, you could easily type one word for the other and spell-check software may not identify the error.

Parental pertains to one's parents; **parenteral** refers to a method of administering a drug, or perhaps nourishment.

prone/supine

Another confusing combination, these terms refer to positions. **Prone** means lying face down on one's stomach. **Supine** means lying on one's back. Here's a hint to keep them straight: when you lie **supine** you are lying on your **spine**.

prospective/retrospective

Folks with a limited knowledge of statistics and clinical trial design tend to confuse these terms. Both words refer to the design of a clinical study. A **prospective** study is one in which investigators develop a study plan and enroll test subjects before executing the study. They evaluate subjects' responses to the treatment under investigation as they are going through the trial. In this type of trial, subjects can be divided into different groups, with one group receiving one type of care while the other receives a different one, or perhaps a sham, or placebo, treatment (this is what's called a placebo-controlled trial). Prospective trials can be blinded, that is, the subjects, investigators, or both have no idea which subjects receive which treatments. Subjects' responses to treatment are monitored for safety and efficacy over a pre-established period of time.

In contrast, a **retrospective** study is a trial in which patients have already undergone some type of treatment or intervention, and the investigators decide, after the fact, to examine patient outcomes. **Retrospective** trials are not blinded, nor are they placebo-controlled. One type of **retrospective** trial would be a chart review, for example, of patients who entered the emergency department with a diagnosis of migraine to determine what type of treatment they received and what types of outcomes they demonstrated.

You may be wondering why I used **subject** in the first paragraph for this entry and **patient** in the second. More on that later in this chapter.

prostate/prostrate

I often hear laypersons using these terms interchangeably. My guess is, though, now that direct-to-consumer advertising has become standard practice, most folks have heard the term **prostate** often enough to recognize that it refers to the male gland near the bladder that can become enlarged and cause problems. **Prostrate** means to lie prone. Nothing shouts INEXPERIENCED like the writer who confuses these very different terms.

regime/regimen

Promise me that after reading this book you won't confuse these terms again. **Regime** usually refers to a system of government; **regimen** refers to a specific system of diet, exercise, or drug administration that is used for a therapeutic purpose. For purposes of their health, patients follow drug **regimens** not **regimes.**

sight/site/cite

These words are called homophones; they sound the same, but have different spellings. Therefore, it's easy to use them incorrectly. Proof your work carefully to be sure you haven't used the wrong term.

Sight is a noun that refers to the sense of vision: "The patient's **sight** was diminished." It also refers to something that is seen: "The medical students needed a break so they went to Las Vegas and saw the **sights**."

Site is also a noun; it means a location: "The **site** of the tumor made it difficult to resect."

Cite is a verb that means to refer to, or to quote: "All references must be *cited* in text."

subject/patient

This might seem like a minor distinction, but when writing about the individuals who participate in clinical trials, it becomes important. A *subject* refers to a volunteer who takes part in a clinical study. This individual does not have a particular disease or condition.

In contrast, a *patient* refers to an individual who is being treated for a particular disease or condition. If an individual has elevated BP and enters a trial to evaluate a new medication to control high BP, you would refer to him or her as a *patient* rather than a *subject*.

thrombus/embolus

It's easy to confuse these terms since they both refer to a blood clot, but it's vital that you use them correctly when you're writing. A *thrombus* is a blood clot that forms within a blood vessel or, sometimes, within an organ, such as the heart. A *thrombus* is stationary, meaning that it does not move from where it originated.

In contrast, an *embolus* (or *embolism*) is a blood clot that forms within a blood vessel and then travels through the body to another location. Some *embolisms* travel to the lungs or the heart, where they can cause big problems. The plurals of these terms are *thrombi* and *emboli.*

track/tract

Medical writers who are just starting out often use these terms interchangeably. Don't do it. A *track* is a path over which something moves (like a train), or the evidence it leaves behind: "Needle *tracks* were visible on the arm of the drug addict."

Tract refers to an anatomic area that usually is long and made of bundles of nerve fibers: "The digestive *tract* includes the esophagus, stomach, and small and large intestines."

vicious/viscous/viscus

I've never heard of a fluid being *vicious*, but I've sampled some that are *viscous*.

Vicious is an adjective referring to demeanor: "The *vicious* dog attacked the doctor when he was leaving his office."

Viscous refers to density and resistance to flow: "The *viscous* medicine was too thick to pour."

Viscus is a noun that applies to any of the large internal organs located in the chest or abdomen. The plural form of this term is *viscera*: "During the autopsy the pathologist removed and weighed the *viscera*."

Some Other Terms That Just Might Stump You

O kay, you might want to stop and take a deep breath. Believe it or not, there are still more terms medical writers need to be familiar with and these might not necessarily be in those expensive medical dictionaries.

Here are some terms I learned through experience, but I wish I had known them when I was starting out. It would have made my life so much easier! They are a combination of medical, health care, insurance, marketing, and writing/publishing terms.

510(k)

This refers to Section *510(k)* of the Food, Drug and Cosmetic Act, which requires manufacturers of medical devices to notify the FDA, at least 90 days in advance, of their intent to market (sell) a medical device. Such notification is also known as Premarket Notification, PMN or *510(k)* for short. By law, medical device manufacturers must submit a premarket notification to the FDA if they plan to sell a completely new device or reintroduce a device that has been changed in a way that might compromise its safety or effectiveness. These could be changes in design, material, chemical composition, energy source, manufacturing process, or how the device is intended to be used. This notification enables the FDA to evaluate the device and determine whether it is equivalent to any that are already on the market. For additional information about *510(k)* clearance, go to: http://www.fda.gov/CDRH/510khome.html.

Algorithm

Algorithms are used quite frequently in the medical arena as tools to aid physicians and other health care professionals in clinical diagnosis or treatment decision-making. Think of an **algorithm** as a branched pathway, sort of like a decision tree, that begins with a question to be answered or a symptom to be considered, such as "Does the patient exhibit nausea and vomiting?" If the answer's yes, the **algorithm** branches in one direction. If the answer is no, the **algorithm** branches in a different direction. Depending on what you're writing, an **algorithm** may be a better way to explain a process than plain text.

Black box warning

Every prescription drug on the market today has written product information that details the diseases and conditions it is approved to treat, along with its risks and benefits. Go to your favorite search engine, type in the name of a drug (for our purposes here let's use the drug Tegretol®), plus the words "prescribing information," and you'll find the prescribing information for this antiseizure medication. When you bring up the full US prescribing information for this drug, on the first page you see boxed text with the heading, WARNINGS. This is the **black box warning**.

For certain drugs that have severe risks or very serious side effects, the FDA requires the pharmaceutical industry to list these major safety risks at the beginning of the prescribing information, where prescribers—and patients, for that matter—can easily find them. The FDA doesn't want these risks to be buried in the document.

Not every drug has a **black box warning**, and some drugs receive **black box warnings** only after they have been on the market for a while since some side effects may not appear until after the drug has been used in larger numbers of patients and for longer periods of time.

I don't want to be accused of pointing out only one drug with a **black box warning**. So, for fair balance, some others with **black box warnings** are Advair®, Enbrel®, Viagra®, and an entire class of drugs known as fluoroquinolones.

Branded

We are exposed to brands and branding every day, from the brand of orange juice we drink with breakfast, to the brand of laundry detergent we use to wash our clothing. The same concept holds true for the medicines and medical supplies we buy, whether it's the brand of over-the-counter pill to relieve our headache or the bandage we put on our skinned knees. I don't know about you, but I prefer to buy one particular brand of analgesic, and I usually buy one specific brand of bandages.

Pharmaceutical companies spend a lot of time and money developing their brands and coming up with catchy names for their products. These names often carry a registered symbol, ®, or a trademark symbol, ™, to indicate that these names are proprietary. You may not know this, but drug names have to be approved by the FDA, so not only is the FDA concerned about whether a drug is safe and effective, it is also concerned about how the pharmaceutical company will be promoting that product to the prescribers and users. From a writing perspective, anything you produce that includes the name of a specific drug is considered to be **branded** material. Here's a fictional example to help you better understand this concept.

Let's say you're working with your client, a medical communications firm, to write some patient-education brochures about a new drug that's designed to treat writer's block. The new drug is called **WriteMor™**; it belongs to a class of drugs called synaptic-reflex enhancers. (Keep in mind that this is not a real class of drugs; I'm only imagining it.) The pharmaceutical company wants one of the brochures to be **branded**, the other to be unbranded.

In the **branded** brochure, you are free to mention the name of the product as often as necessary; however, in the unbranded brochure, you will not be able to mention the brand name, only the drug class. For fair balance, which I discuss later in this chapter, you'll need to mention other drug classes used to treat the condition, as well.

Carcinoma in situ

The phrase, **in situ**, is Latin for "in its place." **Carcinoma in situ** refers to a cancer in the very early stages, when the malignant cells have not yet invaded surrounding tissues.

Cohort

You'll find this term used to refer to certain clinical trials, for example, **cohort** studies. A **cohort** is a group of something that is similar. So, a **cohort** study is a study of patients with similar characteristics, such as age, sex, and disease.

Detail aid

A **detail aid** is a promotional brochure used by sales representatives to explain the product they're selling when they call on health care professionals. Sales reps take the **detail aid** with them on their sales calls and **detail** from it the specifics about their product. Of various lengths, **detail aids** generally include lots of graphs, figures, images, and bullet points (rather than straight text) to communicate quickly the company's key messages about the product. Quick is the key concept here, since doctors usually have a limited amount of time to spend with sales reps.

Disclosure

It's very likely that you will be asked to provide a **disclosure** for some of the materials you produce. This simply means that you are being asked to reveal any associations or relationships you have with the company that is funding whatever it is you are writing.

Disclosures are necessary in today's regulatory environment. Here's an example. Let's say you are working with a medical education firm who invited several physicians to participate in a roundtable discussion about a new and emerging surgical technique they are using. You are asked to put together a newsletter summarizing the contents of that discussion and incorporating the physicians' comments as expert commentary.

You and the faculty members are required to **disclose** any relationships you have with the company that is promoting this technique (and providing funds for the roundtable and the newsletter), and other companies with similar techniques. So, the doctors may indicate that they have received funds from Pharma Company ABC and have been paid to be part of Pharma Company XYZ's Speaker Bureau. If you own stock in Pharma Company ABC, you'll need to **disclose** this relationship. These **disclosures** are printed within the document, so that readers can look for any potential conflicts of interests or any associations that might bias the information that is presented.

Having something to **disclose**, such as a relationship with a pharmaceutical company, does not necessarily mean that what you write—or what the physicians say—is biased. It does provide the transparency, however, into industry-physician and industry-writer relationships that is required.

The **disclosure** discussion leads naturally to a discussion about the use of medical writers who work with physician authors to develop manuscripts for publication in medical journals. This issue reared its head once again in the media, in an article published in the December 12, 2008 issue of the New York Times and in an article published in the December 13, 2008 issue of the Wall Street Journal.

The articles cite an investigation by Senator Charles E. Grassley into whether pharmaceutical giant Wyeth recruited and paid physicians to put their names on journal manuscripts that were already written. This particular situation is just one part of an ongoing investigation by Senator Grassley, a member of the Senate Finance Committee who is trying to determine what, if any, influence the pharmaceutical industry has on physicians.

An unfortunate consequence of this article was the naming of a reputable medical communications firm, whom Wyeth hired to assist with the creation and placement of these journal manuscripts and, indirectly, the suggestion that such firms—and the medical writers they hire—inherently engage in unethical practices when crafting manuscripts.

While my business partner and I recognize that pharmaceutical companies are in business to make money, the suggestion that medical writers and medical communications firms are inherently unethical couldn't be farther from the truth. Have questionable and possibly deceptive practices taken place in the past? We're sure they have. As we write in our book, *The Accidental Medical Writer,* once upon a time, it was perfectly acceptable to keep the contribution of medical writers invisible. More recently, we're pleased to report, the contributions of medical writers have begun to come out of the shadows and be rightfully acknowledged. Of course, with this acknowledgement comes responsibility—including the responsibility of medical writers and others who contribute substantially to the content of a manuscript, to report any potential conflicts of interest. Today, medical writers and medical communications firms must adhere to strict guidelines when it comes to creating journal articles that report on the outcomes of clinical trials that will appear in reputable medical journals.

An unspoken issue here that has been overlooked relates to the skills needed to write an accurate yet readable manuscript. Writing is a skill, one that some folks have innately, but one that others must learn. Writers know how to write; physicians know how to diagnose and manage diseases. As writers, we must have a solid understanding of the science behind what we are writing, but we rely on the expertise of the physicians with whom we work to direct us and keep us on track. Likewise, physicians must have a solid understanding of what they want to communicate, but they rely on medical writers to construct informative and understandable prose. It can no more be assumed that a physician can write than that a teacher can cook. Medicine and writing are separate skills with separate prerequisites.

Every pharmaceutical company has a medical writing department with writers who create documents to very precise standards. Medical communications firms exist to assist pharmaceutical companies with those tasks. Such medical writers are skilled at organizing medical information and making complex scientific information readable and understandable. In the same vein, pharmaceutical companies hire statisticians to crunch the results of clinical trials and identify significant trends and outcomes. I've never understood why it's perfectly acceptable to use statisticians to assist physicians with the content of their manuscripts, but unacceptable to use a medical writer to assist physicians in putting their thoughts coherently on paper.

Let's not allow the valuable contributions of medical writers to be thrashed in this controversy. Instead, let's use this as an opportunity to advance the call for all medical writers who are involved in the development of manuscripts for publication in medical journals to be acknowledged for their contributions and held to the same standards of quality and ethics as physician authors. For more information on this subject, check out the *AMWA Position Statement on the Contributions of Medical Writers to Scientific Publications*. You'll find it here: http://www.amwa.org.

Double-blind

This term is another that describes the study design of a clinical trial. A *double-blind* study is one in which both the subjects (participants in the study) and the investigators are unaware of which subjects receive which treatments. Both the subjects in the trial and the investigators conducting the trial are blinded to the treatment (and sometimes to the results), hence, the term *double-blind*.

Let's take this a step further. Since double-blind means that both the subjects and the investigators are blinded, you can extrapolate and figure out that a single-blind trial is one in which either the subjects or the investigators are blinded to the treatment, but not both. Usually it's the subjects who are blinded to the treatment under investigation to avoid the so-called "placebo effect" (see the entry for *placebo* later in this section).

E-learning

This term refers to an educational delivery system in which the material to be learned is presented through some type of electronic means, such as a computer with Internet or Intranet connections or a mobile device. CD-ROMs and DVDs are other media used to provide training via the *e-learning* modality. *E-learning* is a popular method for teaching sales representatives about the new products they will be marketing, since it can be accessed on demand and doesn't require users to travel to training sessions, eliminating scheduling and transportation issues.

Em dash

An *em dash* is a type of punctuation used within a sentence to indicate a pause in thought. Think of it as an aside you want to add for clarity or emphasis. An *em dash* looks like this (—). Its close buddy, the en dash, is another punctuation mark that is half the size of the *em dash*.

It's easy to get carried away with **em dashes**, so think carefully when you use them. Another punctuation mark, such as a comma or a colon, might work just as well.

An **em dash** does not appear on your computer keyboard, so you have to insert it into your document as a special character. To do so in the latest version of Microsoft® Word®, position your cursor where you want to insert the **em dash**, then go to the top toolbar, click on the "insert" tab, move over to the right side of the top toolbar, and click on "symbol." A drop-down box with the symbols you've inserted most recently will appear, but if the **em dash** isn't there, simply click on "more symbols" and scroll through the list until you find it. You can insert it into your document in two ways: double left click it or left click the **em dash** once to highlight it in the chart, then left click on "insert."

Empirical

You'll hear this term often, especially in the field of infectious disease. It means based solely on experience rather than evidence. Here's an example, using an infectious-disease scenario. Let's say a college student arrives at the student-health department with what appears to be a spider bite on his thigh. The physician wisely recognizes that this is no spider bite, but a highly drug-resistant staph infection known as MRSA. She prescribes an antibiotic known to be very effective at treating the bacteria that usually are responsible for this particular staph infection, even though she has no laboratory evidence showing that the infection is indeed MRSA. We can say that the doctor treated the patient **empirically**. She used her experience rather than hard laboratory evidence to determine which antibiotic to prescribe.

Now, let's say that student's infection worsens and the doctor can now extract material from the infected site for laboratory examination. The lab results show that the infection is not caused by staph bacteria, but by other bacteria, against which the medication she previously prescribed is not effective. She discontinues **empirical** treatment and now prescribes a different antibiotic that is focused on the particular organism (this is called pathogen-focused treatment, in case you're wondering). Make sense?

En dash

Another form of internal punctuation, the **en dash** is bigger than a hyphen but not quite as large as an em dash. It looks like this: (–). You'll find an **en dash** used to indicate page ranges in bibliographic entries (pages 22–31) and in place of hyphens in compound modifiers (drug–induced symptoms). Check a style guide for specific rules about its use.

Like the em dash, the **en dash** is not a keyboard character, so you need to insert it as a special character following the procedure I explained before (see em dash).

Fair balance

Fair balance is a term thrown around often on the promotional side of medical writing, especially as it relates to direct-to-consumer advertising. The term comes from the US FDA regulations that state that advertising must present a fair and accurate assessment of the risks as well as the benefits of a drug. (You can read these regulations here: http://edocket.access.gpo.gov/cfr_2001/aprqtr/pdf/ 21cfr202.1.pdf. They are part of the Federal Food, Drug and Cosmetic Act.) That's why when you see an advertisement for a prescription drug on television, you often hear a narrator listing the side effects and contraindications.

Fair balance applies to print materials as well. This means that in promotional materials, you must include both the good stuff and the bad stuff about a product. You can't simply write about all the wonderful attributes of a drug or device without also mentioning the risks. The FDA will pull promotional materials that do not have *fair balance* and fine the pharmaceutical company that is responsible. These are quite hefty fines, I might add, so pharmaceutical companies are very careful about what they write about their products.

Continuing medical education materials also need to include fair balance. You can't mention benefits without noting the risks also. (Continuing medical education has other regulations that have implications for medical writers, but that's a topic for another book.)

Formulary

This is an insurance term that refers to the list of medications a particular health insurer will reimburse. *Formularies* are developed in tiers, or levels, that indicate which medications will be fully reimbursed, partially reimbursed, or not reimbursed at all. Pharmaceutical companies want their new medications to appear on insurers' *formularies* since it is likely to increase the number of prescriptions written. Patients might be more likely to ask their doctors for medications that are on their *formularies*, especially those on the top (or first) tier, because their out-of-pocket expenses will be less.

Generic

It's nearly impossible to work in the field of medical writing without being exposed to the term *generic*. For that matter, it's almost impossible to go to the pharmacy these days to buy a prescription without being asked if you'd like a *generic* form of the prescribed medication.

Earlier in this chapter, I talked about the term *branded* as it relates to pharmaceutical sales and marketing. In the world of prescription medications, once a prescription drug product receives FDA approval, the pharmaceutical company who markets the product has just 5 years of patent exclusivity for that product before another company can come into the marketplace with a replica of that medication. This means that for 5 years, no one can duplicate that product and sell it. But once that patent exclusivity expires, other companies are free to produce and sell another drug that contains the exact same ingredients and treats the exact same condition. This duplicate drug is called the *generic*. It can include the same ingredients as the *branded* product, but it cannot have the same name as the brand, since brand names are proprietary.

HCFA

HCFA is the Health Care Financing Administration, the government agency responsible for administering the government's health care programs. This includes Medicare and Medicaid. Many insurance companies look at *HCFA* coverage decisions as a guideline to determine whether or not they will pay for certain medical treatments, and how much they will reimburse the professionals who provided the treatment. *HCFA* does not pay for treatments it considers to be ineffective or experimental. And its coverage decisions have far-reaching implications. If *HCFA* considers a treatment to be experimental and doesn't provide coverage, it's likely that other health insurers will consider it experimental and deny coverage, too. Knowing *HCFA's* position on treatments is important for companies as they plan sales and promotional strategies for their products.

Kaiser Permanente

Kaiser Permanente is the largest managed-care organization (MCO) in the United States. Known as an integrated MCO, *Kaiser Permanente* is composed of multiple and distinct entities, including the Kaiser Foundation Health Plan, Inc. (which offers prepaid health plans), Kaiser Foundation Hospitals, and the Permanente Medical Groups (physician-owned organizations). Given its size, *Kaiser Permanente* wields much leverage and influence, and its coverage decisions are widely monitored by other third-party payers and by pharmaceutical companies and device manufacturers, as well.

Krebs cycle

Named after the British biochemist Hans Krebs who first described it, the *Krebs cycle* is a naturally occurring process composed of a series of enzymatic reactions. The ultimate byproduct of the *Krebs cycle* is high-energy phosphate compounds our cells use for energy.

The term, *Krebs cycle*, is an eponym, meaning that it was derived from a person's name. Notice, however, that we use no apostrophe here because the cycle does not belong to Sir Krebs, it is merely named after him. You'll often come across eponyms in medical writing: Alzheimer disease, Paget disease of the bone, Babinski reflex, Down syndrome (yes, that's correct; Down's syndrome is no longer acceptable). When you're unsure about using an "s" and an apostrophe, consult a reputable source such as the *AMA Manual of Style, 10ᵗʰ Edition*.

Leader's guide

To understand what a *Leader's Guide* is, you need to know something about pharmaceutical sales. Before sales reps can call on health care professionals and talk about the products they are selling, they must have a solid understanding of the products and the conditions for which they have been approved. Pharmaceutical companies have extensive sales-training programs for their sales reps, where they spend hours learning about the products they will be selling and how to talk about these products with physicians and other health care providers. These training programs are not merely didactic programs; they often include activities and games to better familiarize the sales reps with the products. Obviously, someone must lead these sessions; that's where the *Leader's Guide* comes in.

Think of the **Leader's Guide** as a tool used during pharmaceutical sales-training activities to describe to the leader exactly how to complete the specific training activity. It's a written set of instructions, a "how-to" description of the activity, with very explicit directions on how to conduct the training.

Lunch-n-learn

In the world of pharmaceutical sales and marketing, **lunch-n-learns** have been a staple. This term refers to an activity in which health care professionals are invited to attend a meeting over lunch time to learn about a new product or treatment for a disease, hence the name **lunch-n-learn**. **Lunch-n-learns** are often a mix of lecture and PowerPoint® slides; they can be led by a physician who is knowledgeable about the new treatment under discussion and who is considered to be a key opinion leader by the pharmaceutical company who has asked him to speak. Pharmaceutical companies hire medical communication firms to develop these presentations as part of a global sales and marketing plan. In turn, medical communication companies hire freelance medical writers (or have medical writers on staff) to work with physicians to create professional-looking slides that drive home key points about the product or treatment.

Meta-analysis

This term describes a statistical procedure that combines the results of a least 2 or more separate but related clinical trials and provides a quantitative statistical analysis of the aggregate results. The studies selected for meta-analysis have very distinct and well-defined characteristics, and similar study designs. They are chosen for inclusion in the meta-analysis because they meet predefined criteria. Combining data from a set of studies that used similar methods and procedures, and that have similar, if not identical, study designs, rather than analyzing data from a single study alone, enables statisticians to analyze data for larger numbers of patients and can produce results that have greater statistical significance than those obtained from one study.

Meta-analyses are widely used in the field of medicine. One group that performs meta-analyses and reports on them is *The Cochrane Collaboration*. This organization produces *The Cochrane Database of Systematic Reviews,* a collection of evidence-based reviews and meta-analyses that summarize the results of clinical trials on a variety of health care interventions. Summaries of the reviews are free; full-text reviews are available, but you must become a subscriber. You can subscribe at: http://www.cochrane.org/reviews.

Monograph

Let's discuss this term as it relates to prescription drugs and medical devices. A *monograph*, for our purposes, is a detailed document (think of a research paper) about a certain drug or medical device. Monographs are written for health care professionals and distributed to them so that they can, at their leisure, read in-depth information about the product or device. *Monographs* are highly technical and include information about a product's efficacy, safety, and clinical indications.

Monographs differ from detail aids in that they are much longer, include more text, and are designed for the health care professional as opposed to the sale representative. Whereas the detail aid communicates details about a product usually through bullet points and short, snappy headlines and subheadings, *monographs* go into more detail in an essay-type format.

Off-label use

Off-label use refers to the use of a drug or device in a way that is not yet approved by the FDA. It is also referred to as an unapproved use, or an unapproved new use. Health care providers are permitted to use a drug or device *off label*, that is, in an unapproved manner. Pharmaceutical companies, however, are not allowed to promote their products for such *off-label uses*.

Off-label use is not that unusual, but don't think that doctors just simply decide on a whim to prescribe something *off label* without evidence that the intervention is safe and effective. In the clinical arena, once a drug or device has been approved by the FDA, clinical researchers continue to conduct experiments to see if the product might have additional uses beyond those for which it was approved by the FDA. The outcomes of these trials into *off-label use* often are published in clinical journals read by health care providers. Once substantial evidence exists for the use of a drug or device in another indication, doctors often adopt the practice.

The key here is that even though doctors are using a product *off label*, the pharmaceutical company cannot promote the product for any use except the FDA-approved indication. Doing so can result in hefty fines for the pharmaceutical company who sells the product (and put patients in danger). You can read more about *off-label* use here: http://www.fda.gov/OHRMS/DOCKETS/98fr/FDA-2008-D-0053-gdl.pdf.

Orphan drug

I've always thought this was a very odd term to use to describe a prescription medication. Still, this is a term the US government applies to products developed for the treatment of rare diseases that affect fewer than 200,000 people. The *Orphan Drug Act*, signed into law in the early 1980s, was designed to provide drug companies with incentives to develop products to treat rare diseases. You can read more about *orphan drugs* at: http://www.fda.gov/orphan/.

Placebo

A *placebo* is a fake medication or a sham treatment. You'll sometimes hear it called a "sugar pill." No matter what it's called, a **placebo** is a medication that contains no active ingredients or a treatment that has absolutely no therapeutic value.

Investigators sometimes use **placebos** in clinical trials to prevent test subjects from knowing whether or not they are receiving the treatment under investigation. If some of the test subjects receive **placebos**, the clinical trial is a **placebo-controlled** study. The use of **placebos** can determine if there is a so-called **placebo** effect; that is, subjects show improvement even when they receive treatments or drugs that have no therapeutic value simply because they expect the treatments to work.

Post hoc analysis

If you are working with data from clinical trials, you'll come across this term. A **post hoc analysis** is a statistical procedure that was performed after a clinical study was completed and the expected outcomes were analyzed. It's generally an analysis of some unexpected or unusual outcome (good or bad) that was observed during the clinical trial but was unrelated to the original purpose (or hypothesis) of the study.

Here's an example, a purely imaginary one. Let's say investigators planned a trial for a new oral contraceptive (OC) with a novel new ingredient. They wanted to make sure it was safe and that it prevented pregnancy, so these were the primary outcomes they were examining. During the course of the study, the investigators noticed that the LDL cholesterol levels (that's the bad stuff) for women on this new OC were getting lower as the study progressed compared with women who received a different OC, whose LDL cholesterol levels either stayed the same or increased. This was an unexpected result and one not originally planned. Once the study ended, the investigators completed a **post hoc analysis** to determine the effect of the new OC on LDL cholesterol levels.

The results of a ***post hoc analysis*** might lead researchers to identify areas for future testing. In this example, it may be that the new OC is better at lowering cholesterol than it is at controlling pregnancies. Or perhaps lowering cholesterol is just an added benefit of this new ingredient. Or maybe this effect simply occurred by accident. Whatever the outcome, this extra statistical analysis has the potential to add value to the results.

P value

I'll keep this explanation simple without going into a lengthy discussion about statistical probability. Simply put, ***P value*** is a statistical term describing the probability that a certain outcome might have occurred by chance. ***P values*** represent the results of a statistical test and can be described as statistically significant or not significant.

RAAS cycle

RAAS (pronounced "razz") is an acronym for renin-angiotensin-aldosterone system. You'll also see it written as ***RAS cycle***. Both are acceptable, but ***RAAS*** is more accurate. I won't bore you with all the technical aspects of how the ***RAAS cycle*** works. Just be aware that it is one component in the complex process that controls blood pressure.

Randomized

This is a term that describes one aspect of a clinical trial design. A ***randomized*** study is one in which the subjects (participants) are assigned to different study groups at random. In other words, all the participants have the same probability of being assigned to any of the study groups.

Contrast this to a nonrandomized, or unrandomized, study, where subjects all receive the same kind of treatment, or are allocated to different study groups based on pre-established criteria.

Some writers use this term to describe the subjects in the study, "*The subjects were randomized to one of three study groups.*" In my opinion, writers should avoid using this construction because it is the clinical trial design that is randomized, not the patients. A better sentence would be, "*Subjects were randomly assigned to one of three study groups.*"

Rep guide

This is another term you'll come across if you do any sales-training writing. A ***rep guide*** is another sales-training tool used by the sales reps. It is a separate, printed document that instructs the sales reps how to use the ***detail aid***. It includes images of each page of the ***detail aid***, accompanied by instructions that highlight how to talk to physicians about the information found in the ***detail aid***.

SI units

You're probably wondering, "What the heck are ***SI units***?" That's a good question, and here's the answer. The term, ***SI units***, stands for the International System of Units, a type of metric measurement system used by MOST of the scientific community. As with the standard metric system, though, health care professionals (and laboratories) in the United States have been slow to adopt this system (if at all); they still report scientific measurements in conventional units.

Some biomedical publications require measurements to be converted from conventional units into ***SI units***, or they want measurements reported with a combination of both, especially if the publications serve readers in countries were ***SI units*** are commonplace. That means that writers and editors may need to convert measurements from one system to another. It becomes confusing, and if math is not your thing, you may want to throw up your arms in despair.

For example, the conventional method of reporting creatinine measurements is mg/dL, that's milligrams per deciliter. In **SI units**, it becomes µmol/L, that's micromols per liter. To convert a conventional creatinine value into **SI units**, you need to multiply the conventional measurement by a conversion factor of 88.4. So a creatinine value of 2 mg/dL becomes 176.8 µmol/L.

How do you know what conversion factor to use? Well, you can stop panicking. The *Journal of the American Medical Association* (JAMA) is one publication that uses **SI units**. They provide complete instructions for conversion here, including conversion factors: http://jama.ama-assn.org/content/vol295/issue1/images/data/103/DC6/JAMA_auinst_si.dtl.

Slim-Jim

This is not what you're thinking. I'm not referring to that wonderfully greasy, spicy sausage stick at your grocer's check-out counter, although I have succumbed to them a time or two. No, this **slim-jim** is a term that describes a narrow brochure (turn an 8.5 x 11 sheet of paper sideways and then fold it into thirds) used for different purposes, perhaps patient education or promotion. **Slim-jims** vary in size, depending on the purpose and the budget, and are a combination of text and visuals.

Symposium

Symposium is simply a fancy term for a meeting or a conference that focuses on a certain topic. The plural is **symposia**. In the medical writing world, the term refers to meetings and presentations that are often piggy-backed (held in concert) with the annual conferences of professional organizations, such as the AMA, or the American Academy of Neurology. In this sense, a **symposium** is sort of a mini-meeting that will be of interest to the attendees but is not necessarily part of the official conference program.

Led by experts in the disease state or treatment area under discussion, a *symposium* gives health care professionals an opportunity to learn about new products and treatments and review evidence showing how these new interventions fit into established treatment protocols. A popular use of *symposia* is to design them so that meeting attendees can obtain CME credit by participating. The use of symposia as promotional or CME tools is very strictly regulated and programs must follow specific guidelines.

Systematic review

As health care interventions become more evidence driven, *systematic reviews* take on greater value because of the evidence they bring to the clinical setting. A *systematic review* is a critical and methodic assessment of research that is relevant to a specifically formulated question. When conducting a *systematic review*, investigators pose a question and then attempt to answer it by analyzing the clinical trial data from multiple studies. The investigators clearly identify the kinds of clinical studies they will be analyzing and what methods were used to identify these trials. Unlike a meta-analysis, which always includes a statistical analysis of the pooled results, a *systematic review* may or may not use statistical methods to analyze the combined results of the trials. Some *systematic reviews* simply summarize the aggregate results of the included studies.

Third-party payers

A *third-party payer* is the entity that makes payments for health care services delivered to a patient. It can be an employer, insurance company, a managed-care organization, or a government agency, such as Medicare or Medicaid. You might be wondering who the first two parties are in this relationship. That would be the patient (the first party) and the health care professional (or entity, such as hospital) who provides the health care services (the second party). The entity that pays for the services (the insurer) is considered the third party.

Now is it spelled **payer** or **payor**? In the context of health insurance, it is more correct to spell it **payer**. In the legal field, however, the term **payor** refers to the person responsible for making payments, such as alimony or child support, to the payee.

Verispan

If you work on the promotional side of medical communications, **Verispan** is a company with which you need to become familiar. It's a market-research firm that tracks prescription drug usage and provides companies in the health care industry with market research and sales data, as well as other services. Companies also hire **Verispan** to conduct survey and opinion research they use as they develop their marketing and promotional strategies.

As a writer, you won't be able to independently download and read the reports **Verispan** prepares for a fee for its clients. But oftentimes your clients will share these reports with you so you can incorporate the data into the materials you're writing. Let me clarify that. Companies will rarely give you the actual proprietary reports they've received from **Verispan**; remember, they've paid big bucks for this information. They will instead summarize the important elements of the reports for you. Because this information is proprietary, you need to be very careful that you do not inadvertently or deliberately share it with other clients.

Widows and orphans

Depending on what you're writing, you might hear the graphic designer use these terms. These desktop-publishing terms have been around ever since the days of typesetting. **Widows and orphans** refer to those single words or short phrases at the ends or beginnings of paragraphs that dangle all by themselves at the bottom or top of a page. I'm not really sure which is a **widow** and which is an ***orphan*** (and if you talk to 10 people they'll all have a different opinion), but I do know that they can make the layout look unbalanced and the text difficult to follow. As a writer, you may have to rework some of your sentences so that a word doesn't appear all alone on a line, or so that a subheading doesn't appear at the bottom of a page while the associated text begins at the top of the subsequent page.

Greek Letters and Where to Find Them

My first experience with Greek letters was when I was pledging a sorority as a first-semester college sophomore. During the 4-week pledge period, I was expected to visit the sisters on a regular basis and perform any tasks they asked of me. One request that was quite popular was to have us recite the Greek alphabet from start to finish. It got interesting when we had to hold a lit match and recite the entire alphabet before the match burned out, or burned our fingertips, whichever came first. To this day, I can recite those letters without pause, but I can't always recall their symbols.

So it was with great interest that I realized that the alphabet that had saved me from many demerits was frequently used in the field of medicine. Who'd have thought that something as esoteric as the Greek alphabet would come in handy in my medical writing career? Not every letter of the Greek alphabet is used in medicine, but quite a few are. You'll find them used in statistical formulas (Δ often represents change), in the chemical names for certain substances (α-fetoprotein), and in other technical and clinical terms (γ rays; β blockers).

That's why it's important for you to be able to recognize these symbols and to use them correctly. After all, if you're writing about alpha blockers, and you use the beta symbol, you've made a huge error. I'm not expecting you to hold a lit match as you review these letters, but do familiarize yourself with their symbols.

When you're writing, the question becomes whether to use the Greek letter (α) or the spelled-out word (alpha). Your clients will have a preference, so ASK them. If they want you to use the Greek letter, then do so; however, if they prefer that you spell out the word, follow their request. Just be consistent. If you use the Greek letter in one section of your text, don't spell out the word in another section.

You might be wondering where in the heck to find those Greek letters, since they don't appear on the keyboard. They are special characters you'll need to insert. To do so in the latest version of Microsoft® Word®, position your cursor where you want to insert the character, then go to the top toolbar, click on the "insert" tab, move over to the right side of the top toolbar, and click on "symbol." A drop-down box with the symbols you've inserted most recently will appear, but if the symbol you need isn't there, simply click on "more symbols" and scroll through the list. Once you find the symbol you need, you can insert it into your document in two ways: double left click it or left click the symbol once, then left click on "insert." It's that easy.

That being said, I need to point out that whenever you use symbols that don't appear on the keyboard, you run the risk of having them translate incorrectly if the document you created is converted from one format or program into another. For example, if you are using a word-processing program to write an interactive module that eventually will be converted into a multimedia program using a program like Director®, the symbols may not appear accurately (or even at all) in the final product. To avoid these kinds of problems, I use the spelled-out words, but I always speak with my clients first and tell them why I'm doing so. These up-front discussions can help prevent many miscommunications as the project progresses.

Just like the English language, Greek letters can appear as capitals or in lowercase. In my experience, for medical purposes, most Greek letters are used in their lowercase form; delta and sigma are, however, some exceptions. In the list that follows, the lowercase letters appear first; capital letters are in parentheses. Keep in mind that as writers we are limited by the word-processing programs we use. The Greek letters available to me may look slightly different from the ones in the program you use. They'll also look different depending on the type of font you choose. Since I'm using Arial, a sans serif font, the Greek letters here won't have the little feet on them that you might find elsewhere.

Alpha	α (Α)
Beta	β (Β)
Gamma	γ (Γ)
Delta	δ (Δ)
Epsilon	ε (Ε)
Zeta	ζ (Ζ)
Eta	η (Η)
Theta	θ (Θ)
Iota	ι (Ι)
Kappa	κ (Κ)
Lambda	λ (Λ)
Mu	μ (Μ)
Nu	ν (Ν)
Xi	ξ (Ξ)
Omicron	o (Ο)
Pi	π (Π)
Rho	ρ (Ρ)
Sigma	σ (Σ)
Tau	τ (Τ)
Upsilon	υ (Υ)
Phi	φ (Φ)
Chi	χ (Χ)
Psi	ψ (Ψ)
Omega	ω (Ω)

A Short Course in Acronyms and Abbreviations

You may already be aware that people in the fields of medicine and health care like to use acronyms and abbreviations. Doctors, in particular, use many abbreviations when writing prescriptions or notes in patients' medical charts. The profession is not unique in that respect, though. Every profession has its own set of jargon that confuses the outsider. And that jargon usually includes abbreviations.

What's the difference between an acronym and an abbreviation? An abbreviation is simply a shortened form of a written word or phrase, such as *bpm* (pronounced "bee, pee, em"), which stands for *beats per minute*. An acronym is an abbreviation (since it's a shortened form), said as a word, and formed usually by combining the first letters or other parts of a series of words. For example, *GERD* is an acronym that stands for *g*astro*e*sophageal *r*eflux *d*isease. You pronounce it just as it's spelled, *gerd*, not by saying each individual letter.

Notice that in the previous paragraph the acronyms and abbreviations are created without using periods. The accepted procedure in medical writing today is to avoid the use of periods with acronyms and abbreviations. You will notice, however, that newspapers and other publications in the popular press still use periods after certain abbreviations. That's because these publishers generally use different style guides than medical publishers do. And that's why it's important to ask what style your client prefers when you start a project.

When abbreviating terms in something you are writing, the standard medical writing procedure is to expand the term at first mention and place the abbreviation in parentheses immediately after the term. From that point on, you should use the abbreviation. Here's an example:

The American Heart Association (AHA) announced new initiatives to reduce heart disease in Americans. The AHA advocates at least 30 minutes of daily exercise, coupled with control of hypertension and a reduction in total cholesterol levels.

Using this same example, if I mentioned the AHA later in the document, I would continue to use its abbreviation only.

Pick up a newspaper, and you'll see that newspaper publishers use a different style. They rarely, if ever, put an abbreviation in parentheses after introducing the term. The form they follow, which drives me crazy, by the way, is to use a term in its entirety at the beginning of a piece, and then use its abbreviation later on. What happens is that by the time the abbreviation appears, I have no idea to what it refers. I have to go back and read the beginning of the piece to figure out the abbreviation.

Be aware that abbreviations have different meanings depending on the context and setting. As you review the list that follows, you may find more than one explanation for a particular entry. When you come across this abbreviation as you work, you'll need to take into consideration the context to interpret it correctly.

As I've told you in previous sections, this list does not include every medical abbreviation that's used today. That's a book in itself, and several books of medical abbreviations are available on the market today. (See the resources section for a listing.) I've tried to include some of the more frequently used ones you'll come across, and those that I stumbled over when I started in this business. But, depending on the particular area in which you're working, you won't find the definition for every term you need. Always consult another source if you're unsure.

The Joint Commission, formerly known as the Joint Commission on the Accreditation of Healthcare Organizations (JCAHO) has compiled a list of abbreviations that health care professionals should not use. Although this list was developed primarily to avoid confusion on medical orders and prescriptions, you should familiarize yourself with the terms and their potential problems. You'll find it here: http://www.jointcommission.org/NR/rdonlyres/ 2329F8F5-6EC5-4E21-B932-54B2B7D53F00/0/dnu_list.pdf.

A1C   hemoglobin A1C, a measurement indicating the severity of a patient's type II diabetes

AAA   abdominal aortic aneurysm, a weak spot (or ballooning out) in the abdominal region of the wall of the aorta, the largest artery in the body

AACME   American Academy of Continuing Medical Education, a medical education company with a very clever name that develops continuing medical education activities for health care professionals; not to be confused with the *ACCME*, described later in this chapter

AAN   American Academy of Neurology, a professional organization for clinicians specializing in the field of neurology

ABC   aspiration, biopsy, cytology, medical shorthand indicating that suspect tissue was removed and sent to the lab for examination; in other contexts, airway, breathing, circulation

ABG   arterial blood gas, a laboratory test that measures levels of oxygen and carbon dioxide in the blood, used to determine lung function

ABMS   American Board of Medical Specialties, works with 24 approved medical specialty boards to develop and implement standards in the ongoing evaluation and certification of physicians

ACC   American College of Cardiology, a professional organization for clinicians specializing in the field of cardiology

ACCME   Accreditation Council for Continuing Medical Education, the organization in the United States that accredits continuing medical education activities and provides oversight of those entities that design and implement activities that give ACCME credits to health care professionals

ACCP   American College of Chest Physicians, a professional organization for physicians who specialize in pulmonology, critical care medicine, thoracic surgery, cardiology, sleep, and other chest-related specialties

ACE   angiotensin-converting enzyme, a naturally occurring peptide that causes blood vessels to narrow, which can elevate blood pressure

ACGME   Accreditation Council for Graduate Medical Education, the private, nonprofit organization that evaluates and accredits medical residency programs in the United States

ACOG   American College of Obstetricians and Gynecologists, a professional organization for clinicians who specialize in obstetrics and gynecology

ACT   activated clotting time, a laboratory test that monitors levels of heparin and other anticoagulants

ADD   attention deficit disorder, a condition in which an individual has an extremely short attention span

ADE   adverse drug event, an unexpected or unintended consequence associated with the use of a medication

ADHD   attention deficit hyperactivity disorder, a condition in which an individual has an extremely short attention span coupled with hyperactivity

ADL   activities of daily living, such as bathing, grooming, dressing, feeding oneself

ADME   absorption, distribution, metabolism, and excretion; pharmacokinetic variables describing the action of a drug in the body

ADVAMED   Advanced Medical Technology Association, a group of worldwide medical technology firms that, according to their website, "advocates for a legal, regulatory and economic environment that advances global health care by assuring worldwide patient access to the benefits of medical technology"

AE   adverse effect, adverse event, an undesired consequence of a medical treatment

AED   automated external defibrillator, a portable device used to treat abnormal heart rhythms

A/G ratio   albumin/globulin ratio, a laboratory test used to determine nutritional status or to assess for certain liver and kidney disorders

AHA   American Heart Association, a consumer-oriented organization that aims to prevent stroke and cardiovascular disease through public education; American Hospital Association, a national organization that represents and advocates for all types of hospitals and health care systems

AHRQ   Agency for Healthcare Research and Quality, a division of the US Department of Health and Human Services

AIDS   acquired immunodeficiency syndrome, the disease caused by HIV

ALOS   average length of stay, a calculation of the mean length of time patients remain in a health care facility, often calculated based on diagnosis or treatment

ALT   alanine aminotransferase, a test of liver function, previously was *SGPT*

AMA   American Medical Association, a professional organization for physicians; in other contexts, against medical advice

AMWA   American Medical Writers Association, a professional organization for biomedical communicators

ANCOVA — analysis of covariance, a statistical tool used to analyze the results of a clinical trial

ANOVA — analysis of variance, a statistical tool used to analyze the results of a clinical trial

ANSI — American National Standards Institute, Inc., a private organization that creates and disseminates standards for industry

AP — anteroposterior, a directional term that means from front to back, often used to identify the direction in which an x-ray film or other radiologic examination was shot; in journalism, the Associated Press

ARB — angiotensin II receptor blockers, a class of drugs used for controlling high blood pressure

ARC — AIDS-related complex, a term describing a condition in which patients test positive for HIV, but have only mild symptoms of AIDS

ARD — acid reflux disease, a condition in which the esophagus becomes inflamed and irritated from stomach acid that backs up into the esophagus

ARDS — acute respiratory distress syndrome, a lung disorder

ASHD — arteriosclerotic heart disease, a form of heart disease

ASM — American Society for Microbiology, a

professional organization for clinicians interested in the study of microbes and infectious diseases

AST   aspartate aminotransferase, a test of liver function, previously was *SGOT*

ATLL   acute T cell lymphocytic leukemia, a blood cancer

ATS   American Thoracic Society, an international professional organization for clinicians interested in critical diseases, pulmonary diseases, and sleep-related breathing disorders

AUC   area under the drug concentration-versus-time curve, a pharmacokinetic variable

AUMC   area under the first moment of the drug concentration-versus-time curve, a variable used in pharmacokinetics

AV   atrioventricular is the common and accepted definition of this abbreviation; it pertains to both the atria and the ventricles of the heart; you may also find AV used to refer to arteriovenous

AVM   arteriovenous malformation, a congenital defect in the arteries and veins

BAC   blood alcohol concentration, the amount of alcohol in the blood

BE   barium enema, used in preparation for nuclear imaging tests

BID	twice a day
BM	bowel movement
BMD	bone mineral density, a measure of the strength of the bones
BMI	body mass index, a ratio of your height and weight
BMR	basal metabolic rate, the amount of energy (calories) your body uses
BP	blood pressure
BPM, bpm	beats per minute, a measure of heart rate
BSA	body surface area
BUN	blood urea nitrogen, a laboratory test that is used to measure kidney function
C	cholesterol, the fat (lipid) components of the blood, seen as the C designation in terms such as **HDL-C**; in another context, concentration
CA	cancer; community acquired
CABG	coronary artery bypass graft(ing), pronounced "cabbage," a surgical procedure to treat ischemic heart disease
CAD	coronary artery disease, a form of ischemic heart disease

CAM   complementary and alternative medicine, a category that includes unconventional or less-conventional treatments such as acupuncture and chiropractic manipulation

CAP   community-acquired pneumonia, pneumonia that is acquired by exposure within a community

CAT   computed axial tomography, an x-ray procedure that uses a computer to generate cross-sectional images of the internal organs and structures of the body; sometimes abbreviated as *CT*

CATH   catheter, a hollow tube inserted into the body

CBC   complete blood count, an examination of the various components of the blood

CC   chief concern, chief complaint, the patient's primary problem; whereas the term chief complaint was used by physicians in the past, today it is more acceptable to use the phrase chief concern

CCMEP   Certified Continuing Medical Education Professional, a certification for professionals working in the field of continuing medical education; you can obtain it through the National Commission for the Certification of CME Professionals: http://www.nccme.org

CCU   cardiac care unit, the area of the hospital housing patients with heart problems; critical care unit, the area of the hospital housing patients with severe medical conditions

CDR clinical data report, a compilation of the individual patient data acquired throughout the course of a clinical trial

CDC Centers for Disease Control, the government agency that monitors communicable diseases

CDMS clinically definite multiple sclerosis, applied to patients when a diagnosis of multiple sclerosis can be made based on clinical symptoms

CE continuing education, continued training required of most professionals; in other contexts, clinically evaluable, a term applied to patients (or results) that can be evaluated to determine the clinical effect of a treatment

CF cystic fibrosis, a lung disease

CHD coronary heart disease, an inaccurate and ambiguous term often used in place of ischemic heart disease or coronary artery disease

CHF congestive heart failure, a condition in which the heart does not pump efficiently

CI confidence interval; a statistical term that refers to the range of values within which the true statistic is expected to lie

CIS clinically isolated syndrome, often used to

describe an isolated clinical event

CK   creatine kinase, a naturally occurring enzyme, elevated levels of which can indicate damage to certain muscles or the brain; previously was *CPK*

CL   confidence limit, a term used in statistical analyses; in the context of pharmacokinetics, refers to clearance, the volume of drug-containing fluid (like blood or urine) that is cleared of the drug per unit of time

CLL   chronic lymphocytic leukemia, a blood cancer

C_{max}   maximum concentration of the drug, a variable used in pharmacokinetics

C_{min}   minimum drug concentration measured before the next scheduled dose of the drug, another variable used in pharmacokinetics

CME   continuing medical education, continued training required of most health care professionals

CMS   Centers for Medicare and Medicaid Services, the division of US Health and Human Services that provides online and downloadable information about these government health programs

CNA   certified nursing assistant, one type of health care professional

CNS   central nervous system

CONSORT   Consolidated Standards of Reporting Trials, a group of initiatives developed to ensure that data from clinical trials are reported adequately and in a standard fashion; the centerpiece of these initiatives is the CONSORT statement, which is an evidence-based, minimum set of recommendations that offers a standard way for authors to write about the results of clinical trials; you can download the CONSORT statement here: http://www.consort-statement.org/mod_product/uploads/CONSORT%20Statement%202001%20-%20Explanatory%20document.pdf

COPD   chronic obstructive pulmonary disease, a breathing disorder

COSTART   Coding Symbols for a Thesaurus of Adverse Reaction Terms, a tool used by clinical investigators to report adverse events

CPE   complete physical examination

CPK   creatine phosphokinase, a type of enzyme; see ***creatine kinase***

CPR   cardiopulmonary resuscitation, a method of external chest compressions meant to continue blood flow through the body in the event of a heart attack

CPT®   Current Procedural Terminology, a system developed by the AMA that assigns unique codes to every medical procedure and service

CRC colorectal cancer, cancer of the colon and/or rectum

CrCL creatinine clearance, a measure of kidney function

CRNA certified registered nurse anesthetist, masters-prepared advanced-practice nurses who administer anesthesia and monitor patients during surgery

CRO contract research organization, an organization to which pharmaceutical companies outsource some or all of their clinical research activities; in another context, cathode-ray oscilloscope, a common laboratory instrument

CRP C-reactive protein, a protein that occurs naturally in the body, elevated levels of which have been linked to heart disease

CRS chronic rhinosinusitis, inflammation, drainage, congestion, and other sinus symptoms that persist despite treatment

CSA chronic stable angina, a form of heart disease

CSF cerebrospinal fluid, the fluid that circulates within your spinal cord and surrounds your brain

CSR clinical study report, a written summary of clinical methods and outcomes submitted to regulatory agencies for review; in another context, Cheyne-Stokes respiration, an abnormal breathing pattern

C$_{ss}$ concentration of the study drug in plasma at steady state, a pharmacokinetic variable

cSSTI complicated skin and soft-tissue infection, an infection that invades the skin and the soft tissue beneath, usually caused by bacteria

CT computed tomography, an x-ray procedure that uses a computer to generate cross-sectional images of the internal organs and structures of the body; sometimes abbreviated as *CAT*

CV coefficient of variation, a statistical term; curriculum vita, a term for a professional's resume

CVA cerebrovascular accident, a stroke

CVD cardiovascular disease, heart disease

CVU cardiovascular unit, the hospital area housing patients with heart problems

D, d day(s)

D & C dilation and curettage, a medical procedure in which cells from the lining of the uterus are removed for further examination

D/C discontinue, to stop

DIC	disseminated intravascular coagulation, an acute condition that might cause unexplained bleeding and clotting
DJD	degenerative joint disease, a painful condition in which the joints degenerate over time
DM	diabetes mellitus, a disease in which the body either does not produce enough insulin or the insulin it produces does not adequately control blood sugar levels
DMD	Duchenne muscular dystrophy, a progressive and degenerative muscle disease
DME	durable medical equipment, a term used by Medicare and other providers to describe equipment such as wheelchairs, hospital beds, and other devices used in a patient's home
DNA	deoxyribonucleic acid, the building block of the human body
DNR	do not resuscitate, medical orders that prevent any life-extending treatments to be performed
DO	Doctor of Osteopathy, an osteopathic physician
DOA	dead on arrival
DOG	desogestrel, an ingredient found in some oral contraceptives (try to avoid using humorous abbreviations such as this one)

DRG   diagnosis-related group, a national system developed by Medicare that classifies hospital cases into defined groups based on diagnosis, age, sex, procedures performed, and the presence of comorbidities; Medicare uses DRGs to determine how much to reimburse hospitals for services, since patients in the same category are expected to use a similar level of resources

DRNG   drainage, seepage from a wound or opening in the body

DRSG   dressing, a bandage applied to a wound

DTC   direct to consumer, advertising directed toward the user of a drug or medical device, rather than to the person who will be prescribing it

DTR   deep tendon reflex, an involuntary movement in response to a stimulus used to evaluate integrity of the central nervous system

DVT   deep vein thrombosis, a blood clot

DX, Dx   diagnosis

EB   evidence base(d)

EBL   estimated blood loss

EBM   evidence-based medicine, a common term these days that refers to care that is provided based on definitive evidence from clinical trials

EBP	evidence-based practice, another term for **EBM**
EBV	Epstein-Barr virus, a common human virus that attacks a person's immune system
ECG	electrocardiogram, electrocardiography, a type of electrical study and recording of heart function
ED	emergency department; erectile dysfunction, the inability to achieve an erection
EDC	expected date of confinement, used to identify a pregnant woman's due date
EDTA	edetic acid, an amino acid used in food preservation, cosmetics, and other industries
EE	ethinyl estradiol, an ingredient in some oral contraceptives; erosive esophagitis, a condition characterized by inflammation of the esophagus
EEG	electroencephalogram, electroencephalography, a type of electrical study and recording of brain function
eg	for example
EGHP	employer group health plan, a health insurance program that provides health coverage to employees, families, and former employees of a company that makes varying employee health-plan contributions
EKG	electrocardiogram, electrocardiography; the

preferred abbreviation now is **ECG**

EM	emergency medicine, medical care provided during an emergency
E$_{max}$	maximum effect, a pharmacokinetic variable
EMG	electromyogram, electromyography, an electrical study and recording of muscle activity
EMR	electronic medical records, a relatively new approach that reduces paper files and computerizes a patient's medical records into one central electronic file
EMS	emergency medical service, the entity that supplies emergency medical care outside of the hospital
ENG	electronystagmogram, a test used to diagnose certain inner ear disorders, like ringing in the ears and unexplained dizziness
ENT	ears, nose, and throat
EP	evoked potentials, electrical signals generated by the nervous system; ectopic pregnancy, a pregnancy that develops outside of the uterus
ER	extraction ratio, a pharmacokinetic variable; in other contexts, emergency room; also can mean extended release to describe medication
ERIC	Educational Resources Information Center, a

searchable database of education-related literature

ESR
erythrocyte sedimentation rate, a nonspecific marker of inflammation

ESRD
end-stage renal disease, severe kidney disease

ESS
endoscopic sinus surgery, minimally invasive surgical treatment for chronic sinus disease performed with an endoscope

et al
and others

ETOH
ethanol, alcohol

EVP
evoked potential, electrical signals generated by the nervous system

F, f
female; in pharmacokinetics, this abbreviation means bioavailability, that is, the fraction of the drug dose that reaches the systemic circulation

FAS
fetal alcohol syndrome, a group of symptoms seen in children born to women who consumed unhealthy amounts of alcohol during pregnancy

FBS
fasting blood sugar, a laboratory test to determine if your blood sugar is within a healthy range

FDA
Food and Drug Administration, the government organization that regulates prescription and nonprescription products in the United States

FESS — functional endoscopic sinus surgery; surgery performed through an endoscope as a treatment for sinus disease that does not respond to medication

FFP — fresh frozen plasma, the plasma portion from blood that is frozen soon after donation

FFS — fee for service, a traditional reimbursement system in which the service provider is paid for each service performed

FH — family history

FMH — family medical history

FP — for profit; false positive, a test result that appears positive when in reality it is negative

FPO — for placement/position only, a graphic design term

FSH — follicle-stimulating hormone, a hormone in both men and women that regulates growth, development, puberty, and reproduction

FTE — full-time equivalent

FTT — failure to thrive, a condition in which infants and children fail to grow and develop at a normal rate

FUO — fever of undetermined origin, a fever for which no cause can be found

Fx, FX   fracture, a broken bone

GA   glatiramer acetate, a treatment for multiple sclerosis

GAD   generalized anxiety disorder, a mental-health disorder; gadolinium, a contrast agent used in certain imaging to differentiate between normal and abnormal tissue (GAD is not the preferred abbreviation for gadolinium, but you may find it used this way)

Gd   gadolinium, a contrast agent used in certain imaging tests to differentiate between normal and abnormal tissue

GDM   gestational diabetes mellitus, diabetes that develops in some women while they are pregnant

GEP   Gene Expression Profiling, a test used to determine which patients have a high risk of cancer recurrence

GERD   gastroesophageal reflux disease, a condition in which the stomach contents back up into the esophagus

GFR   glomeruler filtration rate, a laboratory test considered to be the best way to measure kidney function

GI   gastrointestinal, relating to the stomach and intestines

GMT	Greenwich mean time
GP	general practitioner, a doctor that practices general medicine
GPP	Good Publication Practice, guidelines designed for pharmaceutical companies and other organizations that sponsor clinical trials; these guidelines provide recommendations for how these entities should create industry-sponsored publications for biomedical journals; you can read these guidelines here: http://www.gpp-guidelines.org/
GPO	group purchasing organization, an entity that enables groups (such as hospitals and nursing homes) to leverage their size and purchasing power to negotiate discounts with vendors
GTT	glucose tolerance test, a test to determine how the body responds after ingesting a large amount of glucose
gtt	drop, used on prescription labels
GU	genitourinary, relating to the genital and urinary tracts
H & P	history and physical, referring to a patient's medical history and the physical examination
HA	hospital acquired, a condition acquired while the patient was admitted to a health care facility

HAP   hospital-acquired pneumonia, a respiratory disease acquired while the patient was admitted to a health care facility

HBV   hepatitis B virus, a virus that infects the liver

HCFA   Health Care Financing Administration, often pronounced "hick–fuh," this entity has responsibility for administering the government's health care programs

HCP   health care professional, a skilled practitioner working in some area of health care

Hct, HCT   hematocrit, the proportion of the blood that carries red blood cells

HCV   hepatitis C virus, a virus that infects the liver

HD   Huntington disease, a genetic disorder

HDL   high-density lipoprotein, a form of cholesterol that is often referred to as the "good" cholesterol

HEENT   head, ears, eyes, nose, and throat, part of the physical examination

Hep A   hepatitis A, a liver disease

Hep B   hepatitis B, a liver disease

Hep C   hepatitis C, a liver disease

HIB   haemophilus influenza B, the virus that causes a form of the flu

HIPAA   Health Insurance Portability and Accountability Act, a law enacted by Congress in 1996 that established national standards for patient privacy

HIV   human immunodeficiency virus, the virus that causes AIDS

HLA   human leukocyte antigen, proteins found in most cells of the body that are used to match donors and recipients of organ transplants

HMO   health management organization, a type of health insurance provider

HPV   human papilloma virus, the virus that causes genital warts and cervical cancer

HR   heart rate

HTN   hypertension, high blood pressure

Hx   history, background information about a patient's past, as it relates to medical concerns

IB   investigator's brochure, a document distributed to the individuals who will be conducting and overseeing a clinical trial

ICAAC   Interscience Conference on Antimicrobial Agents and Chemotherapy, an annual conference sponsored by the American Society for Microbiology and the Infectious Diseases Society of America

ICD
International Classification of Diseases, an international system that assigns a numeric code to specific diseases, symptoms, and complaints; implantable cardioverter defibrillator, a device implanted into the heart that constantly monitors heart rate and rhythm and distributes an electrical impulse when necessary to maintain normal rate and rhythm

ICMJE
International Committee of Medical Journal Editors, originally known as the Vancouver Group, this group of editors of medical journals developed a document entitled, *Uniform Requirements for Manuscripts Submitted to Biomedical Journals: Writing and Editing for Scientific Publication*; according to the website, the document identifies "the ethical principles in the conduct and reporting of research and provide[s] recommendations relating to specific elements of editing and writing"; you can read the requirements here: http://www.icmje.org/

ICP
intracranial pressure, pressure within the brain

ICU
intensive care unit, an area of a health care facility reserved for patients who need specialized care and close monitoring

I & D
incision and drainage, a procedure that cuts into infected tissue and drains the fluid

IDDM   insulin-dependent diabetes mellitus, a form of diabetes in which the patient must take regular doses of insulin to regulate blood sugar levels

IDSA   Infectious Diseases Society of America, a professional organization for clinicians interested in the study of microbes and the infections they cause

ie   such as

IEP   individualized educational plan, an educational document developed for any student that needs educational programming out of the norm

IHD   ischemic heart disease, a heart condition that results from impaired blood circulation to the heart

IM   intramuscular, in the muscle; in another context, infectious mononucleosis, a contagious disease

IMRT   intensity-modulated radiation therapy, a type of treatment for certain types of cancer

IND   investigational new drug, this refers to the applications companies must file in order to get permission to test a promising new drug in humans

INR   International Normalized Ratio, a laboratory test that measures how long it takes the blood to clot

IPA   independent practice association, a group of

independent physicians that provides services to managed care organizations for a predefined negotiated rate

IPF
idiopathic pulmonary fibrosis, a progressive condition in which the lung tissue hardens over time and eventually the individual cannot breathe without the use of supplemental oxygen

IRDS
infant respiratory distress syndrome, a breathing disorder present at birth

ISMPP
International Society for Medical Publication Professionals, a professional organization for medical publication professionals involved in medical publication planning and development

ITP
idiopathic thrombocytopenia purpura, a condition in which the person has an extremely low platelet count for no apparent reason

ITT
intent to treat, a term that refers to an analysis of the outcomes for the participants in a clinical trial based on the initial treatment intent

IUC
intrauterine contraceptive, a form of birth control

IUD
intrauterine device, a form of birth control

IV
intravenous, through the veins

IVIG
intravenous immune globulin, a blood plasma product administered through the veins

IVP intravenous pyelogram, a radiologic test used to identify abnormalities in the kidneys, ureter, and bladder

IVU intravenous urogram, see *IVP*

JC Joint Commission, the entity that oversees and accredits hospitals and other health care systems in the United States; see *JCAHO*

JCAHO Joint Commission on the Accreditation of Healthcare Organizations, now known simply as the Joint Commission; see *JC*

KOL key opinion leader, an expert in a particular field

KUB kidneys, urethra, bladder

LA left atrium, a chamber of the heart; lupus anticoagulant, an inhibitor that prevents clotting

LD learning disability, an educational label applied to students who have difficulty learning or who learn in unusual ways; in another context, Lyme disease, a disease contracted from a tick bite

LDL low-density lipoprotein, a form of cholesterol often referred to as the "bad" cholesterol

LE lupus erythematosus, an autoimmune disease; the more accurate term is systemic lupus erythematosus

LGHP large group health plan, a type of health insurer

that provides health insurance to at least 100 employees

LH luteinizing hormone, a hormone produced by the pituitary gland

LLQ left lower quadrant, the lower left region of the torso

LOC loss of consciousness

LOS length of stay, a way to measure how long a patient remained in a health care facility

LP lumbar puncture, a procedure in which a needle is inserted into the space surrounding the spinal cord to extract cerebrospinal fluid for examination

LPN licensed practical nurse, a type of health care professional

LUQ left upper quadrant, the upper left region of the torso

M, m male; lower case can refer to month; in pharmacokinetics it means metabolite

MANOVA multivariate analysis of variance, a statistical tool

MAT mean absorption time, a pharmacokinetic variable that is the mean time involved in the body for the release and absorption processes to take place

MCO   managed care organizations, a type of health insurance provider

MCT   medium-chain triglyceride, a fat that improves absorption of vitamins and minerals

MD   medical doctor; physician; muscular dystrophy

MDI   mental development indices, developmental tests administered to infants and toddlers to evaluate their mental growth and development

ME   microbiologically evaluable, a term applied to people or samples that can be examined for the presence of certain microbes

MEC   medical education company, an organization that designs and implements continuing medical education activities

MEDDRA, MedDRA   Medical Dictionary for Drug Regulatory Affairs, specific terminology applied to all phases of drug development

MFS   Medicare fee schedule, the rates at which Medicare reimburses clinicians for their services

MHS   multihospital system, an organization that owns and/or manages more than one hospital

MI   myocardial infarction, a heart attack

mITT, MITT   modified intent to treat, a term that refers to an analysis of the outcomes for the participants in a

	clinical trial based on the initial treatment intent and exclusions based on predefined baseline criteria
mm Hg	millimeters of mercury, the unit of measure when assessing blood pressure
MMA	Medicare Modernization Act, passed in October 2003, this legislation impacted the payment rate for physicians
MMWR	Mortality and Morbidity Weekly Report, a weekly publication distributed by the CDC
MOA	mechanism of action, how a drug works
MR	mental retardation, mentally retarded, impaired intellectual functioning
MRA	magnetic resonance angiography, a nuclear imaging tool that can measure blood flow throughout the body
MRI	magnetic resonance imaging, a nuclear imaging tool that uses a strong magnetic field to obtain images of internal structures of the body
MRSA	methicillin-resistant *Staphylococcus aureus,* a potentially lethal bacterial infection that is extremely resistant to certain common antibiotics
MRT	mean residence time, a pharmacokinetic variable that is the average time necessary for

intact drug molecules to move through the body

MS multiple sclerosis, a progressive degenerative disease; in the *do not use* category, morphine sulfate, magnesium sulfate, both medications

MSA metropolitan statistical area, a core urban area composed of a large population

MSSA methicillin-susceptible *Staphylococcus aureus,* a potentially lethal bacterial infection that can be treated with certain antibiotics

MV mitral valve, a valve in the heart

MVA motor vehicle accident, a car crash

N, n number, often used in figures and tables to indicate how many patients participated in a clinical trial, or how many patients were in a particular subset for analysis of outcomes

NA not applicable; not available; nursing assistant

NABS neutralizing antibodies, a term that describes antibodies that sometimes develop in patients undergoing treatment for multiple sclerosis

NCCME National Commission for the Certification of CME Professionals

NCLB No Child Left Behind Act, federal legislation requiring public schools to meet certain performance requirements

NDA new drug application, a formal regulatory process that pharmaceutical companies must go through to receive FDA approval for their drug

NFP not for profit, a term often applied to groups that provide health care or health insurance coverage; NFPs are not seeking to earn a profit, but often do

NH nursing home, a facility that provides long-term care; sometimes called a skilled-nursing facility

NICU neonatal intensive care unit, a specialized hospital unit for infants with special or severe medical conditions, or who have been born prematurely

NIDDM noninsulin-dependent diabetes mellitus, a form of diabetes in which the patient does not require insulin to regulate blood sugar levels

NIH National Institutes of Health, the federal agency that conducts and supports medical research

NK natural killer, a term describing certain cells in the body

NLM National Library of Medicine, a division of NIH, it is the world's largest medical library

NMR nuclear magnetic resonance, the term applied to certain radiologic imaging techniques

NNH number needed to harm, the number of patients

who, if they received an intended treatment, would lead to 1 additional person being harmed

NNT   number needed to treat, the number of patients who need to receive a particular treatment in order to prevent 1 additional negative outcome (such as death)

NOTES   natural orifice transluminal endoscopic surgery, a new surgical approach that removes elements through the natural body cavities, eliminating the need for incisions

NP   nurse practitioner, a primary health care provider

NPO   nothing by mouth, this means that the person cannot eat or drink anything

NSAID   nonsteroidal anti-inflammatory drug, a type of medication used to reduce inflammation

NSR   normal sinus rhythm, a normal heartbeat

OB   obstetrics, the field of medicine that specializes in caring for expectant mothers and delivering babies

OCD   obsessive-compulsive disorder, a mental-health disorder

OD   right eye; overdose; Doctor of Optometry

OIG   Office of the Inspector General, a division of the US Department of Health and Human Services

(HHS), the OIG's mission is to protect the integrity of HHS programs and the health and welfare of the beneficiaries of those programs

OR   operating room

OS   left eye

OT   occupational therapy, occupational therapist, the health care professional that teaches patients to perform activities of daily living, such as dressing; in another context, over time

OTC   over the counter, the term describing drugs and drug products that can be purchased without a prescription

OU   both eyes

P & A   percussion and auscultation, an examination of the chest in which the examiner uses a stethoscope to listen to the heart and lungs

PA   posteroanterior, a directional term meaning from back to front; in other contexts PA means physician assistant

PAD   peripheral artery disease, a condition in which blood flow to the legs is reduced, causing pain of varying degrees

PBI   protein-bound iodine, one measure of thyroid function

PCI percutaneous coronary intervention, a treatment for ischemic heart disease

PCOS polycystic ovary syndrome, a complicated health problem that includes a range of symptoms that can affect the menstrual cycle, fertility, and weight, among others

PCP primary care physician/provider, a family doctor; phencyclidine, angel dust, an intravenous anesthetic sometimes used illegally as an illicit drug; *Pneumocystis carinii* pneumonia, a form of pneumonia that often develops in people infected with HIV

PCR polymerase chain reaction, a technique widely used in molecular biology

PCV packed cell volume, the fraction of the whole blood volume that contains red blood cells

PD pharmacodynamics, the study of a drug's effects in the body and its mechanisms of action

PE pulmonary embolism, a blood clot that traveled to the lungs

PET positron emission tomography, a diagnostic imaging tool

PharmD Doctor of Pharmacy, a pharmacist

PhRMA Pharmaceutical Research and Manufacturers of America, the entity that represents the nation's leading pharmaceutical and biotechnology companies; PhRMA disseminates guidelines for the implementation of clinical trials, as well as direct-to-consumer advertising, health outcomes research, and the pharmaceutical supply chain

PI product information, prescribing information, package insert, detailed information about a prescription drug's indications and use, dose regimens, precautions, contraindications, and side effects

PID pelvic inflammatory disease, a general term for an infection in the female reproductive organs

PK pharmacokinetics, the study of the action of a drug in the body, including its absorption, distribution, metabolism, and excretion of a substance, usually a drug

PKU phenylketonuria, a genetic disorder

PM postmortem, after death

PMH past/previous medical history

PML progressive multifocal leukoencephalopathy, a rare viral disease

PMS premenstrual syndrome, a group of symptoms associated with the menstrual cycle

PO by mouth

POD
postoperative day (rather than print on demand), a length of time after surgery

POS
point of service, a type of managed care health insurance program

PPH
primary pulmonary hypertension, also known as unknown pulmonary hypertension, a condition in which blood pressure in the pulmonary artery rises for no apparent reason

PPO
preferred provider organization, a type of health insurance provider

PPT
PowerPoint®, a computer program that enables you to create computer-generated slides

PSO
Patient Safety Organization, a private or public entity that wants to improve the safety and quality of health care delivery by collecting and analyzing data on patient safety events; PSOs were created as a result of the Patient Safety and Quality Improvement Act of 2005; learn more about PSOs at: http://www.pso.ahrq.gov/

PT
physical therapy, physical therapist; part-time; prothrombin time, a laboratory test often used to detect bleeding disorders and to determine how well anticoagulants are working

PTT
partial thromboplastin time, a laboratory test that measures common pathways of the coagulation cascade

PTX	pneumothorax, a collapsed lung
PVCs	premature ventricular contractions, a type of abnormality of the heart in which the lower chambers of the heart contract in an abnormal pattern
Px	prognosis, the expected outcome; patient
QHS	every night
QID	four times a day
QOD	every other day
Q_L	liver (hepatic) blood flow, a pharmacokinetic variable
Q_R	kidney (renal) blood flow, a pharmacokinetic variable
RA	rheumatoid arthritis, a chronic and painful disease characterized by inflammation of the joints
RBC	red blood cell, a cellular component of the blood
R & D	research and development, the term applied to the lengthy and complicated process of drug development from beginning to end
RD	retinal detachment, an eye emergency in which the retina becomes separated from its underlying support system

RDA   recommended daily allowance, recommended dietary allowance, the estimated amount of a food or nutrient that is required to maintain adequate health and nutrition

RLQ   right lower quadrant, the lower right region of the torso

RMSF   Rocky Mountain spotted fever, an infectious disease caused by a tick bite

RN   registered nurse, a health care professional

RNA   ribonucleic acid, a component of our cells

R/O   rule out, to eliminate possible causes

ROM   range of motion, the degree to which your joints can move

RR   relative risk, a statistical abbreviation denoting probability of developing a certain outcome

RRR   relative risk reduction, a statistical term

RRMS   relapsing-remitting multiple sclerosis, a form of MS in which symptoms come and go

RT   respiratory therapy, respiratory therapist, the health care professional that assists patients to maintain or improve lung function; in another context, radiation therapy, or radiologic technologist; in a third context, recreational therapy

RUQ	right upper quadrant, the upper right region of the torso
RVU	relative value units, a scale used to determine reimbursement rates for health care providers that takes into consideration geographic and other factors
Rx	prescription
S, s	second(s)
SAD	seasonal affective disorder, a condition in which people react to the reduced amount of light in the fall and winter by becoming lethargic and depressed
SAE	serious adverse event, a potentially life-threatening unexpected event that occurred as a result of a medical treatment
SARS	severe acute respiratory syndrome, a severe and sudden respiratory disease caused by a coronavirus
SC, sc	subcutaneous, a method of drug delivery
SCID	severe combined immune deficiency, a pediatric disorder that leaves children highly susceptible to severe, life-threatening infections
SD	standard deviation, a statistical term
SE	standard error, a statistical term

SEM   standard error of the mean, a statistical term

SGOT   serum glutamic oxaloacetic transaminase, a liver function test now called *AST*

SGPT   serum glutamic pyruvic transaminase, a liver function test now called *ALT*

SIDS   sudden infant death syndrome, a condition in which apparently healthy infants die from no visible cause

SLE   systemic lupus erythematosus, an autoimmune disease

SNF   skilled-nursing facility, pronounced "*sniff*"; a nursing home

SOB   shortness of breath; try to avoid using this humorous abbreviation

SOC   standard of care, the acceptable manner of caring for a patient with a specific condition

SOP   standard operating procedure(s), the established procedure for doing something

S/P   status post, meaning after a particular event

SPECT   single photon emission computed tomography, a type of nuclear imaging scan; see *SPET*

SPET   single photon emission tomography, same as *SPECT*

SPMS	secondary progressive multiple sclerosis, a progressive degenerative disease
SS	steady state, a pharmacokinetic variable that exists when all rates of drug input and elimination are in equilibrium
SSA	Social Security Administration
SSI	surgical site infection, an infection that develops at the site of an incision; in another context Supplemental Security Income, a federal income-supplement program
SSTI	skin and soft-tissue infection, an infection that invades the layers of skin and the soft tissue beneath
ST	speech therapy, speech therapist, the health care professional that treats speech and language disorders
STD	sexually transmitted disease, a disease spread through sexual encounters; in other contexts, skin test dose, referring to allergy testing
SUN	serum urea nitrogen, a type of laboratory test, previously was called ***BUN***
SWOT	strengths, weaknesses, opportunities, threats, a marketing term used to analyze favorable and unfavorable factors that can influence the success of a product; strengths and weakness are internal factors (within the company),

opportunities and threats are external factors (outside of the company)

Sx   symptoms

T_0   lag time, a pharmacokinetic variable that refers to the time before the absorption of a drug following administration

$T_{1/2}$ half-life, a pharmacokinetic variable that measures the time it takes for the concentration of a drug to decrease by 50%

T & A   tonsillectomy and adenoidectomy, procedures that remove the tonsils and adenoids

TB   tuberculosis, a disease of the lungs

TBI   traumatic brain injury, an injury to the brain as the result of some type of accident

TCN   tetracycline, a common antibiotic

TENS   transcutaneous electrical nerve stimulation, the use of electric current through the skin to reduce pain

TIA   transient ischemic attack, sometimes called a ministroke

TID   three times a day

TMJ   temperomandibular joint, the joint that connects the lower jaw (mandible) to the skull

TNM   tumor-node-metastasis, one type of cancer-staging system

TOC   test of cure, clinical trial terminology; in another context, table of contents

TP   total protein, a laboratory test used to determine nutritional status or to assess for certain liver and kidney disorders

TPN   total parenteral nutrition, a method of feeding a person who cannot consume nutrition by mouth

TPR   temperature, pulse, and respiration, vital signs

TSH   thyroid-stimulating hormone, a hormone that is secreted by the thyroid gland

TSS   toxic shock syndrome, a potentially fatal disease caused by certain bacteria

TURP   transurethral resection of the prostate, a surgical technique used for prostate disease

TX, Tx   therapy, treatment

UA   urinalysis, a laboratory test that analyzes the components of the urine

UCR   usual, customary, and regional/reasonable; a rate-schedule formula used by insurers to determine the rates they will pay for certain medical services and treatments

UK	United Kingdom
ULN	upper limits of normal, the uppermost value that is considered to be within the normal range
UNOS	United Network of Organ Sharing, the entity that manages the organ-transplant system in the United States
URI	upper respiratory infection, a cold
US	United States
UTI	urinary tract infection
UV	ultraviolet
V	apparent volume of distribution, a variable used in pharmacokinetic
VAP	ventilator-acquired pneumonia, a form of pneumonia acquired after a patient has been placed on a ventilator for a period of time
VAS	visual analog scale, a tool that measures a specific response (such as pain) along a continuum
VD	venereal disease, today more commonly referred to as a sexually transmitted disease
VLDL	very low density lipoprotein, a type of cholesterol
VS	vital signs, the collective term for heart rate,

	respirations, blood pressure, and temperature
VSS	vital signs stable, meaning that the patient's vital signs are not fluctuating
VZV	varicella zoster virus, one of the herpes viruses that cause chicken pox in children and shingles in adults
WBC	white blood cell, white blood cell count
W/C, w/c	wheelchair
W/H	weight-for-height, a term used when discussing growth percentiles
WNL	within normal limits
Y, y	year(s)
YAG	yttrium-aluminum-garnet, a type of laser

An Introduction to Body Systems

Health care professionals, doctors in particular, have been trained to think of human anatomy in terms of body systems. Most of us who come from nonmedical or quasi-medical backgrounds haven't learned about these systems. We tend to think in terms of diseases or individual body organs. Without an understanding of these systems, writers new to medical terminology may feel lost and confused.

The term, *body systems*, refers to groups of organs that work together to perform a specific function in the body. Some organs perform several different functions and, therefore, are part of more than one body system (the skin, for example). The 11 major body systems to be aware of are (in alphabetical order):

- Circulatory
- Digestive
- Endocrine
- Excretory
- Immune (lymphatic)
- Integumentary
- Muscular
- Nervous
- Reproductive
- Respiratory
- Skeletal

Why do you need to be aware of these systems? For several reasons. Understanding the body systems is important when reporting or explaining the results of clinical studies. Clinical trial investigators collect data on adverse effects; they report on these events according to body system. So when you're told that a new drug adversely affects the lymphatic system, if you think the drug affects the bladder and kidneys, you're making a huge error.

Here's another example. Let's say you're hired to write about a drug used to treat diseases of the integumentary system. If you've never bothered to learn about this system, you wouldn't know that the skin is involved. It's as simple as that.

What follows is a brief description of each system, including its purpose and some of the major organs involved. Let me re-emphasize the word brief. For a more complete discussion of these systems, their component parts, and their functions, take a look at *Gray's Anatomy: The Anatomical Basis of Clinical Practice, 39th edition* (ISBN 978-0443071683) or *Gray's Anatomy for Students* (ISBN 978-0443066122).

The Circulatory System

This system is concerned with delivering oxygenated blood to the cells and organs of the body. The major organs in this system are the heart, arteries, veins, capillaries, the blood, and the spleen, which filters out impurities from the blood.

The Digestive System

This system is concerned with how an individual processes food. Its purpose is to convert food into smaller units that can be absorbed and later used by the body. From an anatomical perspective, the major organs included in this system are the mouth, esophagus, stomach, pancreas, liver, gall bladder, and small and large intestines.

The Endocrine System

This system focuses on the production and secretion of hormones by the body. Its purpose is to regulate growth, development, metabolism, and reproduction. The major organs of this system are the hypothalamus, pancreas, testes, ovaries, as well as these glands: thyroid, pineal, parathyroid, pituitary, and adrenal.

The Excretory System

This system is concerned with how well the body eliminates wastes. It includes any organ that plays a role in that function, including the kidneys, bladder, ureters, urethra, rectum, and, you'll be surprised to know, even the skin and lungs. The sweat glands in the skin remove excess water and salt from the body. The lungs expel carbon dioxide, which is a metabolic waste product.

The Immune (Lymphatic) System

This system helps us to fight disease and defend against agents that cause disease. Other functions include moving lymph throughout the body. Major components of the immune system include the skin, white blood cells, and lymph nodes.

The Integumentary System

I love to say that word, integumentary. It just rolls off the tongue, doesn't it? The purpose of this system is to provide support and protection, regulate temperature, and act as a sense organ. Components of this system include the skin, hair, nails, sense receptors, and sweat glands.

The Muscular System

The purpose of the muscular system is to work with the skeletal and nervous systems to produce coordinated movement. As you might imagine, the major components of this system are our muscles.

The Nervous System

This system focuses on how well the brain and the nerves communicate with each other in response to changes that occur within the body or externally. The major organs of this system include the brain, spinal cord, and nerves.

The Reproductive System

The purpose of this system is to produce sex cells and enable fertilization, development, and birth of offspring. Other functions include producing sex hormones and, with the mammary glands, to provide nourishment. Major components of this system vary depending on one's sex, but include all of the major sex organs.

The Respiratory System

The organs of the respiratory system work together so that the body receives fresh oxygen and eliminates carbon dioxide. The major organs in this system include the nose, lungs, trachea, pharynx, larynx, bronchi, and the diaphragm.

The Skeletal System

The purpose of this system is to provide structural support and protection for our body, and to make red blood cells. The major components of this system are the bones of the body, of which we have 206 (or 208, depending on what source you're using).

Those Pesky Bacteria and How to Write About Them

If you're a freelance medical writer, or thinking about becoming one, infectious disease is one of the many therapeutic areas about which you might be writing. In fact, as I'm writing this book, infectious disease is a rather hot topic, given the rise in drug-resistant bacteria, especially MRSA, in the community. So it should be no surprise that the materials you create for this therapeutic area will include bacterial terminology.

Bacteria and other microscopic creepy-crawlies come in all shapes and sizes. Some of them have very interesting names with foreign-looking spellings that will be quite unfamiliar unless you have a background in microbiology. Here are just a few examples: *Haemophilus influenza*, *Legionella pneumophila*, and *Escherichia coli*.

The scientific naming of these critters, as well as viruses and other living organisms, is called nomenclature. You can see that the nomenclature for bacteria is composed of two parts: the first word in the scientific label identifies the genus and the second word identifies the particular species. So, using one of the examples above, *Legionella pneumophila, Legionella* is the genus and *pneumophila* is the species.

When you are writing about bacteria, you will usually follow the style adopted by the AMA, that is, to use the complete bacterial name (with the genus capitalized, the species lowercase, and the entire name italicized) when you first mention the bacteria in text. When you next mention it, abbreviate the genus portion of the name (that's the first word in the combination). So when I first write about *Staphylococcus aureus* in a document, I'll write it out. Then next time I write about the *S aureus* in the same document, I'll abbreviate the genus, as I've done here, but I'll use the complete species name.

The preferred style by the AMA is to abbreviate the genus without using a period (*E coli*). This current preference differs from the style a few years ago, which was to include a period after the genus abbreviation (*E. coli*). Some clients for whom you'll work may prefer this alternate style, so be sure to ask them at the start of your projects. If they want periods and you don't insert them in your first draft, it will become tedious to go back later and add them in.

When it comes to bacterial abbreviations, I want to throw in a word of caution here. Health care professionals are notorious for using only bacterial abbreviations without first expanding the genus name. This can become a problem because there are several bacteria with genuses that begin with the same letter. *Staphylococcus*, *Streptococcus*, and *Salmonella* are just a few examples. So please don't assume when you see the abbreviation *S faecalis* that the genus is *Staphylococcus*, because it's not. It's *Streptococcus*.

To avoid making mistakes, I recommend you use a book such as the *International Code of Nomenclature of Bacteria*, which is published by the American Society for Microbiology. This reference describes the rules of nomenclature and includes approved lists of bacterial names. Unfortunately, this resource is not available online; however, J.P. Euzeby, a professor of microbiology and immunology, has a useful site entitled, *List of Prokaryotic Names with Standing in Nomenclature*, where you can check out any bacterial names you don't know. You can find the site here: http://www.bacterio.cict.fr/.

Now we come to the question of whether you should consider the term *bacteria* and any of the specific bacterial names as singular or plural terms. Technically, the term *bacteria* is plural; the singular is *bacterium*. The AMA style guide recommends distinguishing between the singular and plural terms, so that when the singular term is intended, the writer should use the term *bacterium*.

What does this mean for writers? Let's say you want to make a statement about the location of the body populated by certain bacteria. You'll, of course, be using the plural, because it will be a rare case for a body to have only one little bacterial microorganism. Here's what you write:

The bacteria is colonized on the skin and in the nares of about 40% of patients admitted for inpatient care.

Have you used the correct subject/verb agreement?

No.

Why? Because the plural term *bacteria* needs a plural verb. That would be *are* rather than *is*. The correct statement should be:

The bacteria are colonized on the skin and in the nares of about 40% of patients admitted for inpatient care.

What if you used the scientific name, *Staphylococcus aureus*, instead of the word *bacteria*?

Staphylococcus aureus is colonized on the skin and in the nares of about 40% of patients admitted for inpatient care.

Then you would be correct. The AMA style guide considers the scientific names of bacterial species to be singular; thus, they require a singular verb.

The Hierarchy of Footnotes or *How the Heck Do I Refer to All These Footnotes in a Table?*

Medical writers spend a lot of time converting complex scientific information into more user-friendly forms. This often means creating tables and figures. Tables and figures are great ways to present dry scientific data in a more interesting format.

Any materials you produce related to pharmaceutical marketing are governed by very strict regulations, however. That means that when you're consolidating detailed data into a table, for example, you'll probably need footnotes throughout to provide additional information that doesn't quite fit into the table proper. Even if you don't originally design the tables with footnotes, it's highly likely that once the medical-legal review team gets its hands on the document, it will insist on placing footnotes selectively within the material. I'm not kidding you about this. I've seen tables that have had as many as 12 footnotes. It becomes unwieldy, but necessary to comply with FDA regulations.

Footnotes are the place to insert explanatory matter, rather than in the column headings or table title. The question becomes how to refer to the footnotes in an organized manner in the body of the table so that readers can figure out what each footnote means. Believe it or not, a hierarchy does exist to guide writers when inserting footnotes. Here goes.

Writers actually have 2 methods from which to choose. (Isn't it nice to have options?) The more traditional method involves the use of specific symbols that don't appear on the computer keyboard. To insert these special characters into a document, use the same procedure I described previously in the section on Greek letters.

Cynthia L. Kryder, MS, CCC-Sp

Footnote Number	Symbol
1	* (asterisk)
2	† (dagger)
3	‡ (double dagger)
4	§ (section symbol)
5	¶ (paragraph symbol)
6	‖ (parallel lines)
7	** (2 asterisks)
8	†† (2 daggers)
9	‡‡ (2 double daggers)

Since this hierarchy limits the writer to only 9 footnotes, some publications have adopted a different alphabetic system. You simply use the superscript letters from *a* to *z* for your footnotes. The first footnote is *a*, the second *b*, the third *c*, and so on. Take note that we are using lowercase letters here, not capital letters.

To superscript a character in the latest version of Microsoft® Word®, go to the font dialog box, click on the button that has this icon, x^2, then type in your character.

With both methods, you determine the order of the footnote by when the footnoted material first appears in a horizontal row of the table. Here's an example:

Title A	Title B	Title C	Title D
Information[a]	Information	Information	Information[b]
More info	More info[c]	More info	More info

[a] Explanation for footnote a
[b] Explanation for footnote b
[c] Explanation for footnote c

Footnote *a* is considered the first footnote because it appears first in the first horizontal row of information. Since English readers progress from left to right, we number footnotes from left to right, as well. Footnote **b** is the second footnote because, reading across that first row of information, that footnoted material appears next. You get the picture.

How do you know whether to use the traditional system or the alphabetic one? Ask! In my experience it's becoming more common to use superscripted letters rather than symbols, especially since some publications also use asterisks to refer to P values in tables, with 1 asterisk (*) for P<0.05, 2 asterisks (**) for P<0.01, and 3 asterisks (***) for P<0.001.

If you are working with an author to prepare a manuscript that will be submitted to a particular medical journal, and the manuscript includes tables, you should review the journal's guidelines for submission. To do so, go to your favorite search engine, type in the name of the journal (I like to put quotes around the journal name), followed by "submission guidelines" or "instructions for authors," or a similar phrase.

Let's use a journal called the *Archives of Internal Medicine* as an example. The first result I get after typing in "Archives of Internal Medicine instructions for authors" leads me directly to a webpage titled *Manuscript Criteria and Information.* When I click on the entry for *Tables*, I can get to a page that describes exactly how to create tables for submission to this journal. The *Archives* prefers footnotes to be lowercase letters rather than symbols, and P values to be reported as exact numbers. So when I'm creating any tables for manuscripts that will be submitted to this journal, I'll do just that.

Yes, You Do Need to Edit Your Work or *How to Make Editors Happy and Get Repeat Business*

As a freelance medical writer with lots of experience, I enjoy sharing what I know with other writers. That's why I lead roundtable discussions and writing workshops for AMWA. Most of the topics I speak on are well attended, but a while ago I lead a roundtable discussion at our chapter's annual freelance workshop entitled, *Yes, Writers Need to be Editors, Too.* Wow! Although I don't have the figures in front of me, I would have to guess that it was the least popular roundtable offered that year.

Can you guess why?

It's because writers like to write, but many of them don't like to edit. At least I've found this to be true in my experience.

When I was fairly new to this business, one of my colleagues told me that she never edited her work. "That's what the editor's for," she said with confidence. She didn't really care if the citations in the bibliography were incomplete or that some of them didn't follow the AMA format. It was her opinion that she was getting paid to write the content; someone else was getting paid to clean up the document, remove any typos, and put it into the company's preferred format.

I have to disagree.

I worked for a period of time as managing editor of a quarterly publication. Although I was not responsible for copy editing the documents we produced, the copy editor kept me in the loop about which writers were careful about the work they did and which ones turned in final drafts filled with typos and other errors. The company was in its infancy, and we were operating on a tight budget. I was expected to get the publication out within budget or, better yet, under budget. If I'm paying a copy editor by the hour to edit, and she spends 5 hours editing one writer's work but needs 15 hours to edit another's, which writer do you think I'll contact in the future? I don't care how personable, attractive, or responsive a writer is, if he or she can't follow specific style guidelines and can't even perform a careful spell check on the final draft, I'm going to think twice about hiring him or her again.

This is how editors think. If they tell you that they want all references cited in the document to follow AMA style, you better figure out how to do it. And that means EVERY reference. Just because you can't remember how AMA cites chapters in textbooks, that's no excuse for not doing it that way. Crack open the style guide and figure it out. Don't assume the editor is going to be willing—or able—to correct your mistakes. The final draft should be as perfect as you can make it.

If I sound as though I'm standing on a soapbox, I am. I get aggravated when writers produce sloppy work. It reflects badly on them, but it also reflects badly on the freelance writing profession as a whole.

Don't get me wrong, though. I recognize that freelance medical writers are often hampered by time constraints, specifically tight deadlines imposed upon us by our clients. It's difficult to produce creative and accurate work when you feel pressed for time. Still, that shouldn't keep you from performing a simple spell check before you send the document on its way, nor should it prevent you from printing out a hard copy of your document and reading it for mistakes and formatting issues (such as missing line spaces).

Yes, you read that correctly. I'm advocating printing out hard copies of your work. This advice may not sound very "green" in today's reduce/reuse/recycle environment, but in my experience, I've learned that errors jump out at you more readily on a hard copy than they do on screen. Perhaps that's because we are so used to looking at a computer screen when we write that looking at something in a new medium activates a different part of our brain. That's just my theory, but I know that even after I've reviewed a document a couple of times electronically, I'll always find a few more mistakes in the printed copy.

If you're concerned about paper use, do what I do. I recycle all paper that has been printed on only 1 side and use this to print out review copies. Just make sure you load the sheets into the paper tray correctly so that the copy prints on the unused side.

One editing tip that writers share is to hide whatever you've written in a drawer for a day or two, then pull it out and read it with a fresh pair of eyes. Putting some distance between you and the project does make a difference. That paragraph you thought was so brilliant on Monday morning may not seem so wonderful on Thursday afternoon.

So please, I'm begging you, if you want to succeed in the field of freelance medical writing, take responsibility for the words you put on paper and make time to edit your work. It's a competitive world out there, and with the US economy, as well as the global economy, looking more precarious with each passing week, you need to have an edge that differentiates you from the thousands of other freelance medical writers in the world. Consistently delivering accurate work on time will go a long way in making your clients happy and putting you on the short list of writers they'll consider for future work.

If you read *The Accidental Medical Writer*, you've heard this before, but it's worth mentioning again: Keeping a client (customer) is easier than getting a new one. That's why you want to do everything you can to keep the clients you have coming back to you.

Resources

As I mentioned before, one of the features of the books in *The Accidental Medical Writer* series is the list of resources that appears in every book. My business partner, Brian, and I are working freelance medical writers with almost 40 years of collective freelance medical writing experience. We've uncovered a lot of books, websites, and databases that we rely on every day and we want you to become familiar with them, too.

Before going any further, I'd like to share one thought about electronic resources you find on the Web. A large amount of medical information exists on the Internet. Some sites are more credible than others. The sites we list are ones we have found to be reputable. Always consider the sponsor and/or author of the site when determining the reliability of the information you find there. And do check the date to see when the site was last updated. You want to avoid using out-of-date information.

Knowing about the resources that follow can make your life as a freelance medical writer easier and make the quality and accuracy of your writing better. Using some of these resources has the potential to make you a better writer, and that ultimately will make you more appealing to prospective clients.

For Grammar, Spelling, and Usage

- ***American Medical Association's Manual of Style, 10th Edition***; ISBN 978-0195176339. This guide for authors and editors is indispensable on your bookshelf. With few exceptions, most clients you'll be working for will follow this style guide.

- ***The Chicago Manual of Style: The Essential Guide for Writers, Editors, and Publishers, 15th edition***; ISBN 978-0226104034. Although most of the clients with whom you'll be working will follow the AMA style manual, occasionally you'll encounter one who follows this style guide. You can obtain a free, 30-day trial to the online version of this resource (with the ability to print selected pages) but you need to register with a valid email address at: http://www.chicagomanualofstyle.org.

- ***Eats, Shoots & Leaves*** by Lynne Truss; ISBN 978-1592400874. This is a very clever book that actually makes punctuation fun!

- ***The Elements of Style, 4th Edition*** by William Strunk and E.B. White; ISBN 978-0205309023. This style guide, which has been around for years in one edition or another, is an essential tool for writers in any genre.

- ***Lapsing Into a Comma: A Curmudgeon's Guide to the Many Things That Can Go Wrong in Print—and How to Avoid Them*** by Bill Walsh; ISBN 978-0809225354. First of all, I have to say that I love this title and I wish I had thought of it first! The author, copy chief for the Washington Post, provides an opinionated and funny discussion about applying basic grammar rules to contemporary grammar issues.

- ***Medical English Usage and Abusage*** by Edie Schwager; ISBN 978-0897745901. In this reference text, the author, who is a long-time member of AMWA, an AMWA fellow, and the author of the *Dear Edie* column in the *American Medical Writers Association Journal,* reviews some principles of medical communications and provides explanations to enhance understanding.

- ***Merriam-Webster's Collegiate® Dictionary, 11th edition***; ISBN 978-0877798095. Even working as a medical writer, you'll still need a dictionary that shows you how to spell good old English words. After registering for free, you can search the dictionary online at: http://www.merriam-webstercollegiate.com /noauth/ mwlogin.php?return=/.

Medical and Health Care Terminology

- **Dana-Farber Cancer Institute Dictionary of Medical Terms**. The Dana-Farber Cancer Institute is a well-respected cancer-treatment facility. The hospital has created this online, searchable dictionary to help patients and their families understand common terms they'll encounter in the clinical-trial and general-practice environments. The dictionary defines a large number of cancer-related terms, including drugs used to treat cancer and those being evaluated in clinical trials. This is a website you can trust for information about cancer: http://www.dana-farber.org/can/dictionary/.

- **Dorland's Illustrated Medical Dictionary, 31st edition**; ISBN 978-1416023647. An indispensable resource in my personal library, this dictionary provides definitions for almost any medical term you'll come across.

- **Gray's Anatomy: The Anatomical Basis of Clinical Practice, 39th edition** by Susan Standring (the 40th edition is set to be published soon); ISBN 978-0443071683. This is the most complete book on human anatomy you'll ever find.

- **Gray's Anatomy for Students** by Richard Drake, Wayne Vogl, and Adam Mitchell; ISBN 978-0443066122. This textbook is a wonderful resource for anyone just becoming familiar with the field of medicine. It explains anatomy using easy-to-understand terms and colorful diagrams.

- **International Code of Nomenclature of Bacteria** (1990 Revision) by S. P. Lapage, Editor; ISBN 978-0555810392. Published by the American Society for Microbiology, this is a useful (but rather pricey) resource to have on your bookshelf if you do a lot of writing in the fields of microbiology and infectious disease.

- ***Jablonski's Dictionary of Medical Acronyms and Abbreviations with CD-ROM*** by Stanley Jablonski; ISBN 978-1416058991. This 6th edition of a popular paperback reference also includes a handy CD-ROM you can install in your computer.

- ***List of Prokaryotic Names with Standing in Nomenclature*** by Dr. J. P. Euzeby. The author of this site, a professor of microbiology and immunology, provides useful lists of bacterial terminology that will come in handy if you write in the fields of microbiology and infectious disease: http://www.bacterio.cict.fr/.

- ***Medical Acronyms, Eponyms & Abbreviations*** by Marilyn Fuller Delong; ISBN 978-1570665059. Written by an experienced nurse and writer, the latest 4th edition of this reference is a must have for your bookshelf.

- ***Medical Terminology for Health Professions*, *5th edition*** by Ann Ehrlich and Carol L. Schroeder; ISBN 978-1401860264. Even though this book and accompanying materials are meant to be used as part of a medical-terminology course, writers will find it to be a complete source for all the medical terms they'll encounter.

- **Medical Terminology Web Program**. Developed by William J. Dyche, PhD for Des Moines University, this free online program takes a sequential approach to learning medical terms. No registration is necessary. Use the buttons on the left margin to proceed through the program if you don't want to take any of the periodic quizzes that appear throughout the program: http://www.dmu.edu/medterms/.

- **MediSpell™ Spell Check Software**. This is just one example of medical spell-check software programs on the market today: http://www.medispell.com/.

- **MedTerms.** MedTerms is a searchable, online medical dictionary that is part of MedicineNet.com. This reference provides easy-to-understand explanations for more than 16,000 medical terms. Keep in mind that the definitions are written in plain language so consumers and patients can understand them: http://www.medterms.com/script/main/hp.asp.

- **mediLexicon**. Another searchable, online medical dictionary, mediLexicon provides definitions for terms, phrases, acronyms, and abbreviations. Powered by *Stedman's Medical Dictionary* and geared more toward professionals, this site defines more than 100,000 medical terms, so chances are you'll find what you need: http://www.medilexicon.com/medicaldictionary.php.

    If you want to search specifically for an abbreviation, go to: http://www.medilexicon.com/medicalabbreviations.php.

- **MedLine Plus® Health Information.** A resource of the US National Library of Medicine and the National Institutes of Health, this informative and searchable website includes a dictionary and medical encyclopedia, as well as summaries of more than 750 different health topics. Links to external sites allow you to access additional information quickly. This is a very user-friendly site: http://www.nlm.nih.gov/medlineplus/medlineplus.html.

- ***Orthopaedic Dictionary*** by Stanley Hoppenfeld and Michael S. Zeide; ISBN 978-0397513116. This specialized dictionary defines terms you aren't likely to find in typical medical dictionaries and contains hundreds of helpful illustrations.

- **RadiologyInfo™.** This site, developed jointly between the American College of Radiology and the Radiological Society of

North America, is a searchable resource for anything related to radiology. It includes a glossary of terms, descriptions of radiologic procedures and treatments, and explanations of the equipment used: http://www.radiologyinfo.org/index.cfm?bhcp=1.

- ***Stedman's Medical Abbreviations, Acronyms and Symbols, Fourth Edition on CD-ROM*** edited by Stedman's (who produce a popular medical dictionary); ISBN 978-0781772907. This electronic reference for medical acronyms and abbreviations lists more than 75,000 entries. It is also available as a downloadable file with search capabilities.

- ***Visible Body*™** by Argosy Medical Animation. This is a wonderful site that includes a comprehensive, 3-dimensional, fully animated human anatomy model, with complete models of all the body systems. You need to register in order to access this web-delivered application, but it's free. I think you'll be surprised once you see it. Go to the website to view the system requirements to make sure your computer can handle it: http://www.visiblebody.com/.

Health Care Coverage (Including Health Insurance and Managed Care Terminology)

- **Centers for Medicare and Medicaid Services.** This searchable site offers information about the US Medicare and Medicaid programs. You can obtain general information about the services provided to Medicare and Medicaid recipients, search for statistics on various health care trends and outcomes, and review and download National Coverage Determinations (NCDs) and Local Coverage Determinations (LCDs), local policy articles, and proposed NCD decisions. Included in the site are several other types of national coverage policy-related documents, including national coverage analyses (NCAs), coding analyses for labs (CALs), Medicare Evidence Development & Coverage Advisory Committee (MedCAC) proceedings, and Medicare coverage guidance documents. The site also includes a searchable glossary of acronyms commonly used by Medicare and Medicaid. The home page from which you can navigate to the various databases is here: http://www.cms.hhs.gov/.

- **Managed Care Digest Series®.** Developed and distributed by the pharmaceutical giant, sanofi-aventis, this annual series of free hard-copy or electronic digests includes the *Hospitals/Systems Digest*, the *Senior Care Digest*, the *eManaged Care Trends Digest*, the *Government Digest*, and the *HMO-PPO Digest*. You won't go to this site for a dictionary or glossary; however, the individual digests contain information about all the major components of health care delivery and provide updated information and statistics incorporating data from Verispan. For example, the *Government Digest* features a comprehensive overview of the Medicare and Medicaid programs, including data on Medicare prescription drug coverage and common diagnoses and procedures of Medicare beneficiaries and Medicaid recipients in hospitals. Each digest is downloadable from the site. Be sure to click on the "Access Digest Data" button on the toolbar at the top: http://www.managedcaredigest.com/.

- **Managed Care Glossary of Terms, Second Edition.** This site is developed and administered by The Network: A Collaboration to Improve Medical Education and Health Care, formerly The California Managed Care Education and Research Network. The online glossary is searchable by initial letter only, but it offers a rather extensive list of insurance terms as well as acronyms. One drawback: it expands the acronyms but does not explain them, so although you'll be able to figure out what the letters stand for, you might not understand all of the managed care terms and concepts without an explanation: http://futurehealth.ucsf.edu/cnetwork/resources/glossary/intro.html.

- **Managed Care Terminology.** This website provides alphabetized but unsearchable definitions of the most common terms used in managed care. It was developed by the US Department of Health and Human Services and is fairly complete, but if you want to be able to search quickly, this is not the site for you: http://aspe.hhs.gov/Progsys/forum/mcobib.htm.

- **SAMSHA's National Mental Health Information Center Managed Care Glossary**. This website is one component of the Substance Abuse and Mental Health Services Administration (SAMSHA), a division of the US Department of Health and Human Services. It provides an alphabetical listing of managed care terms, including those related to mental health conditions that you might have to write about: http://mentalhealth.samhsa.gov/publications/allpubs/mc98-70/default.asp.

Educational Terms and Concepts

- **Educational Resources Information Center (ERIC®).** ERIC is a national information system that enables you to search and access education-related literature. The ERIC database contains almost 1 million abstracts of documents that focus on education research and practice. You'll find the ERIC system homepage here: http://www.eric.ed.gov/.

- **LD Online.** This site offers a glossary of specialized educational terms and acronyms (searchable by alphabet letter), as well as expert-reviewed articles on learning disabilities and ADHD. I find this landing page a good place to start: http://www.ldonline.org/indepth/glossaries/glossary_of_acronyms.html. To go directly to the glossary, click on the glossary button on the left sidebar.

- **Learning Circuits Glossary.** At this page you'll find a searchable listing of terms associated with e-learning. It's helpful to be familiar with some of these terms, especially if you're asked to create an e-learning module for sales training program or some other type of interactive program: http://www.learningcircuits.org/glossary.html.

Subject Index

Blood urea nitrogen, 96
BM, 96
BMD, 96
BMI, 7, 96
BMR, 96
Body mass index, 7, 96
Body surface area, 96
Body Systems
  Circulatory System, 138
  Digestive System, 138
  Endocrine System, 139
  Excretory System, 139
  Immune (Lymphatic System), 139
  Integumentary System, 139
  Muscular System, 140
  Nervous System, 140
  Reproductive System, 140
  Respiratory System, 140
  Skeletal System, 140
Bone mineral density, 96
Both eyes, 123
Bowel movement, 96
BP, 96
bpm, 87, 96
brachy–, 26
Brachycephaly, 26
brady–, 26
Bradycardia, 17, 26
Branded, 61
bronch, bronchi, broncho, 37
Bronchoscope, 37
Bronchoscopy, 37
BSA, 96
BUN, 96, 131
By mouth, 125
C, 96
CA, 1, 2, 96
CABG, 96

CAD, 96
Callous/Callus, 49
CAM, 97
Cancer, 2, 96
CAP, 97
carcin, carcino, 37
Carcinoma, 18
Carcinoma in situ, 62
cardi, cardio, 37
Cardiac care unit, 97
Cardiomegaly, 41
Cardiopulmonary resuscitation, 100
Cardiovascular disease, 102
Cardiovascular unit, 102
CAT, 97
cat–, cata–, 26
Cataphoria, 27
Cataplexy, 20, 27
CATH, 97
Catheter, 97
Cathode-ray oscilloscope, 101
CBC, 97
CC, 97
CCMEP, 97
CCU, 97
CDC, 98, 119
CDMS, 98
CDR, 98
CE, 98
–cele, 14
celphalo, 28
Centers for Disease Control, 98
Centers for Medicare and Medicaid Services, 99, 160
Central nervous system, 100
cephal, cephalo, 37
Cephalopathy, 38
Cerebrospinal fluid, 101

Concentration of the study drug in plasma at steady state, 102
Concomitant, 27
Confidence interval, 98
Confidence limit, 99
Congestive heart failure, 98
Consolidated Standards of Reporting Trials, 100
CONSORT, 100
Continuing education, 98
Continuing medical education, 6, 69, 97, 99
contra–, 27
Contract research organization, 101
Contraindication, 27
COPD, 100
Coronary artery bypass graft, 96
Coronary artery disease, 96
Coronary heart disease, 98
COSTART, 100
CPE, 100
CPK, 99, 100
CPR, 100
CPT, 3, 7, 100
Craniotomy, 19
CRC, 101
CrCL, 101
C-reactive protein, 101
Creatine kinase, 99, 100
Creatine phosphokinase, 100
Creatine/Creatinine, 49
Creatinine clearance, 101
Critical care unit, 98
CRNA, 101
CRO, 101
CRP, 101

CRS, 101
CSA, 101
CSF, 101
CSR, 101
C_{SS}, 102
cSSTI, 102
CT, 102
Current Procedural Terminology, 100
Curriculum vita, 102
–cusis, 15
CV, 102
CVA, 102
CVD, 102
CVU, 102
cyst, cysti, cysto, 38
Cystic fibrosis, 98
cyt, cyto, 38
–cyte, 15, 36
D & C, 102
D, d, 102
D/C, 102
dacry, 38
Dacryogenic, 38
dacty, dactyl, 38
Dana-Farber Cancer Institute Dictionary of Medical Terms, 156
Day, Days, 102
de–, 27
Dead on arrival, 103
Decalcify, 27
Deep tendon reflex, 104
Deep vein thrombosis, 104
Degenerative joint disease, 103
dent, denti, dento, 39
Dentition, 39
Deoxyribonucleic acid, 103

infra–, 30
Inframandibular, 30
INR, 114
Insulin-dependent diabetes
  mellitus, 114
Intensity-modulated radiation
  therapy, 114
Intensive care unit, 113
Intent to treat, 115
inter–, 30
Intercapillary, 30
International Classification of
  Diseases, 113
International Code of
  Nomenclature of Bacteria,
  142, 156
International Committee of
  Medical Journal Editors, 113
International Normalized Ratio,
  114
International Society for
  Medical Publication
  Professionals, 115
Interscience Conference on
  Antimicrobial Agents and
  Chemotherapy, 112
intra–, 30
Intra-articular, 30
Intracranial pressure, 113
Intrahepatic, 30
Intramuscular, 114
Intrauterine contraceptive, 115
Intrauterine device, 115
Intravenous, 115
Intravenous immune globulin,
  115
Intravenous pyelogram, 116
Intravenous urogram, 116
intro–, 30

Introduction, 30
Introitus, 30
Investigational new drug, 114
Investigator's brochure, 112
IPA, 114
IPF, 115
IRDS, 115
Irregular, 29
Ischemic heart disease, 114
ISMPP, 115
–itis, 17, 38
ITP, 115
ITT, 115
IUC, 115
IUD, 115
IV, 115
IVIG, 115
IVP, 116
IVU, 116
Jablonski's Dictionary of
  Medical Acronyms and
  Abbreviations with CD-ROM,
  157
JC, 116
JCAHO, 89, 116
Joint Commission, 116
Joint Commission on the
  Accreditation of Healthcare
  Organizations, 89, 116
Kaiser Permanente, 70
Key opinion leader, 116
Kidney disease, 107
Kidneys, urethra, bladder, 116
kines, kinesio, 40
KOL, 116
Krebs cycle, 71
KUB, 116
LA, 116
Lag time, 132

Managed care organizations, 118
Managed Care Terminology website, 161
MANOVA, 117
MAT, 117
Maximum concentration of the drug, 99
Maximum effect, 106
MCO, 118
MCT, 118
MD, 118
MDI, 118
ME, 118
Mean absorption time, 117
Mean residence time, 119
MEC, 118
Mechanism of action, 119
MEDDRA, MedDRA, 118
Medical Acronyms, Eponyms & Abbreviations, 157
Medical Dictionary for Drug Regulatory Affairs, 118
Medical doctor, 118
Medical education company, 118
Medical English Usage and Abusage, 155
Medical prefix, 23
Medical suffixes, 13
Medical Terminology for Health Professions, 5th edition, 157
Medical Terminology Web Program, 157
Medicare fee schedule, 118
Medicare Modernization Act, 119
mediLexicon, 158
Mediolateral, 40

MediSpell™ Spell Check Software, 157
Medium-chain triglyceride, 118
MedLine Plus® Health Information, 158
MedTerms, 158
mega, megal, megalo, 41
melan, melano, 41
Melanism, 41
meno, 41
Menorrhagia, 21
Menorrhagic, 21
Menorrhea, 21, 41
Mental development indices, 118
Mental retardation, 119
Mentally retarded, 119
Merriam-Webster's Collegiate® Dictionary, 24, 155
mesi–, mesio–, meso–, 30
Mesocardia, 30
Meta-analysis, 72
Metabolite, 117
–meter, 17
Methicillin-resistant Staphylococcus aureus, 119
Methicillin-susceptible Staphylococcus aureus, 120
Metropolitan statistical area, 120
–metry, 18
MFS, 118
MHS, 118
MI, 118
micro–, 31
Microbiologically evaluable, 118
Microscope, 31
Microvasculature, 31

–scopy, 22, 35
SD, 129
SE, 129
Seasonal affective disorder, 129
Seborrhea, 21
Second(s), 129
Secondary progressive multiple sclerosis, 131
SEM, 130
semi–, 33
Semicoma, 33
Septoplasty, 20
Serious adverse event, 129
Serum glutamic oxaloacetic transaminase, 130
Serum glutamic pyruvic transaminase, 130
Serum urea nitrogen, 131
Severe acute respiratory syndrome, 129
Severe combined immune deficiency, 129
Sexually transmitted disease, 131, 134
SGOT, 95, 130
SGPT, 130
Shortness of breath, 130
SI units, 77
SIDS, 130
Sight/Site/Cite, 56
Single photon emission computed tomography, 130
Single photon emission tomography, 130
Sinusitis, 17
Skilled-nursing facility, 121, 130
Skin and soft-tissue infection, 131

Skin test dose, 131
SLE, 130
Slim-Jim, 78
SNF, 130
SOB, 130
SOC, 130
Social Security Administration, 131
SOP, 130
spasm, 44
Species, 141
SPECT, 130
Spectrometer, 17
Speech therapist, 131
Speech therapy, 131
Spell-check software, 24, 49, 54, 158
Spermicidal, 15
SPET, 130
SPMS, 131
SS, 131
SSA, 131
SSI, 131
SSTI, 1, 131
ST, 131
Standard deviation, 129
Standard error, 129
Standard error of the mean, 130
Standard of care, 130
Standard operating procedure, 130
Status post, 130
STD, 131
Steady state, 131
Stedman's Medical Abbreviations, Acronyms and Symbols, Fourth Edition on CD-ROM, 159

Transcutaneous electrical
nerve stimulation, 132
Transient ischemic attack, 132
Transurethral resection of the
prostate, 133
Traumatic brain injury, 132
Treatment, 133
tri–, 34
Trisomy, 34
–trophy, 22
TSH, 133
TSS, 133
Tuberculosis, 132
Tumor-node-metastasis, 133
TURP, 133
Twice a day, 96
TX, Tx, 133
UA, 133
UCR, 133
UK, 134
ULN, 134
Ultraviolet, 134
uni–, 34
Unicellular, 34
Uniform Requirements for
Manuscripts Submitted to
Biomedical Journals:
Writing and Editing for
Scientific Publication, 113
United Kingdom, 134
United Network of Organ
Sharing, 134
United States, 134
UNOS, 134
Upper limits of normal, 134
Upper respiratory infection, 134
ur, uri, 44
URI, 134
Urinalysis, 133

Urinary tract infection, 134
US, 134
US Food and Drug
Administration, 7, 107
US Health and Human
Services, 99
Usual, customary, and
regional/reasonable, 133
UTI, 134
UV, 134
V, 134
Vaginal, 14
Vancouver Group, 113
VAP, 134
Varicella zoster virus, 135
VAS, 134
vas, vasculo, vaso, 45
Vasoactive, 45
VD, 134
Venereal disease, 134
Ventilator-acquired pneumonia,
134
Verispan, 7, 80, 160
Very low density lipoprotein,
134
Vicious/Viscous/Viscus, 58
Video disc, 50
Viscera, 58
Visible Body™, 159
Visual analog scale, 134
Vital signs, 134
Vital signs stable, 135
VLDL, 134
VS, 134
VSS, 135
VZV, 135
W/C, w/c, 135
W/H, 135
WBC, 135

CPSIA information can be obtained
at www.ICGtesting.com
Printed in the USA
BVOW08s1702180517
484439BV00001B/151/P